EARTHWORMS

A NEW SERIES

Synopses of the British Fauna
Edited by Doris M. Kermack AND R. S. K. Barnes

The *Synopses of the British Fauna* are illustrated field and laboratory pocket-books designed to meet the needs of amateur and professional naturalists from sixth-form level upwards. Each volume presents a more detailed account of a group of animals than is found in most field-guides and bridges the gap between the popular guide and more specialist monographs and treatises. Technical terms are kept to a minimum and the books are therefore intelligible to readers with no previous knowledge of the group concerned.

Volumes 1 – 18 inclusive are available from the Linnean Society of London, Burlington House, Piccadilly, London W1V 0LQ
Volumes 19 – 28 inclusive are available from the Cambridge University Press.
All subsequent volumes may be obtained from E. J. Brill, Publishing Company, Leiden, The Netherlands.

Edited by Doris M. Kermack and R. S. K. Barnes
No. 31

EARTHWORMS

Keys and notes for the identification and study of the species

R. W. SIMS
*Department of Zoology, British Museum (Natural History), Cromwell Road,
London SW7 5BD*

and

B. M. GERARD
The Edinburgh School of Agriculture, West Mains Road, Edinburgh EH9 3JG

1985
Published for
The Linnean Society of London
and
The Estuarine and Brackish-Water Sciences Association
by
E. J. Brill/Dr. W. Backhuys
London – Leiden – Köln – København

ISBN   90 04 07582 8

Typeset and printed in Great Britain at The Pitman Press, Bath

A Synopsis of the Earthworms

R. W. SIMS
Department of Zoology, British Museum (Natural History), Cromwell Road, London SW7 5BD

and

B. M. GERARD
The Edinburgh School of Agriculture, West Mains Road, Edinburgh EH9 3JG

Contents

Foreword

Earthworms are probably some of the first animals we recognise when we are children, as they are usually abundant in our gardens. Yet our early fascination fails to last into adulthood, so earthworms have not received the detailed attention that is normally expected of so abundant an animal. Their use, usually mis-identified, in school biology classes only exceptionally enhances later interest and surprisingly there are few books devoted to these invertebrates despite Darwin's classic work (Darwin, 1881).

This *New Series Synopsis No. 31* should provide the means for the earthworms used in biology classes and found in ecological surveys to be correctly identified and show that there is no animal called 'the earthworm' and that many genera and species inhabit British soils. The distribution of the different genera is influenced by the moving boundaries of the Ice Ages of the Pleistocene and Quaternary Periods in Europe and there is evidence that the world-wide distribution of the different families is and was at the mercy of Continental Drift. Much more recently, economic and social factors such as the importing into the British Isles of pot-plants, fruits and vegetables from overseas has led to the inclusion of so-called exotic species in the British fauna. As our homes are warmer today than at the beginning of the century, it is possible that even more exotic species than those recorded in this synopsis will be introduced in the future. It is important that these introductions along with alterations in our endemic earthworm fauna due to changing land use should be recorded and reported to the Biological Records Centre (see Data Recording p. 38).

This *Synopsis* records the use of earthworms to break down slurried manure, particularly in pig-farming, and the subsequent extraction of the resultant large population of worms to be later fed to the livestock as a protein supplement to their food. Earthworm-farming is a comparatively recent development in the search for new sources of protein. The farming of many more vertebrates for human consumption will produce a demand for earthworms with their ability to cope with the partially digested cellulose found in manure and turn it into usable protein. The 'traditional' culturing of worms for a bait still remains and populations have been used in agriculture and horticulture to improve the condition of the soil. Earthworms should therefore not be despised and this synopsis will assist in showing their true worth and potential.

Earthworms is written jointly by Reginald Sims of the Annelida Section of the British Museum (Natural History) in London and Brian Gerard of the Edinburgh School of Agriculture. This *Synopsis* follows the *New Series* format and contains over fifty figures, many of which are composite; few will recognise it as a third edition of *Synopsis No. 6 – Lumbricidae* by the late L. Cernosvitov and A. C. Evans of Rothamsted Experimental Station and published in 1947 with only nine figures. A second edition written by Brian Gerard was produced in 1964. It is always a pleasure to report that an author of an original series synopsis is an author of one with a similar title in the *New Series*. The Editors thank the authors for the care, trouble and time they have taken in the preparation of their manuscript and illustrations. Few will mourn the demise of 'the earthworm'.

R. S. K. BARNES,
Estuarine & Brackish-water Sciences
Association.

DORIS M. KERMACK,
Linnean Society of
London.

Introduction

Earthworms form the dominant component in the animal biomass of the soil. They play a highly significant role in the soil ecosystem by participating in organic matter cycles and modifying soil structures. They make nitrogen available for plant growth by feeding on organic matter in the soil then voiding casts with a low Carbon/Nitrogen ratio, the latter often containing fragmented litter which in turn is readily broken down by micro-organisms. Changes in the physical structure of the soil are brought about by ingested soil particles being ground down then casted to produce a finer soil, and by earthworm burrows improving soil aeration and drainage. Surface casting activity over a long period can bury stones, even archaeological sites, as was first recognized by Darwin (1881).

Earthworms belong to the phylum Annelida consisting of coelomate animals that have the body divided into a series of compartments, or segments, by thin transverse walls, or septa, with a coelomic fluid filling the cavity containing the internal organs; externally they have a few short bristles, or setae, on most body segments. Together with small aquatic worms (naids, tubificids, lumbriculids etc.), the ubiquitous potworms, or iceworms, (enchytraeids) and the Asian moniligastrid earthworms, they form the class Oligochaeta. Also included in the phylum are the related classes of the marine bristleworms (Polychaeta), the leeches (Hirudinea) and some minor groups. The term 'earthworm' is restricted in this *Synopsis* to apply only to the worms called 'megadriles' by the older authors, i.e. Oligochaeta assigned to the suborder Lumbricina. This distinction is necessary since there is no group vernacular name for these worms in English unlike, for example, German in which they are termed *Regenwürmer* = 'rain worms'. Thus other soil-dwelling Oligochaeta such as the potworms, family Enchytraeidae, are excluded from this present *Synopsis* as they are 'microdriles' and belong to the suborder Tubificina together with the small aquatic Oligochaeta. In any case, only a few Enchytraeidae are found in the soil as most are aquatic, many being marine. (Since the members of this family are so ecologically diverse, the potworms will form the subject of a separate *Synopsis*.)

About half of the 6000 or more described species of Oligochaeta are earthworms. The majority of the earthworms of Europe belong to the family Lumbricidae but only about two dozen species are found in the British Isles although another half-a-dozen or so species of other families have successfully survived adventitious introduction into these islands from other continents. The small number of British species is in sharp contrast to tropical countries where the earthworm faunas may be large, and even nearby in

France where some 180 species have been recognized (Bouché, 1972). This paucity of species in British reflects the slow dispersal rates of earthworms and the comparative brevity of the period when continental species had opportunity to colonize Britain between the final retreat of the Pleistocene ice sheets and the formation of the North Sea and the English Channel.

General structure

The body of an earthworm is approximately cylindrical in shape but the posterior region may occasionally be quadrangular, octagonal or trapezoidal in cross-section while, in the case of some surface browsing species (*Lumbricus terrestris* (p. 106), *L. friendi* (p. 102)), depressed i.e. flattened dorso-ventrally. Size is variable, among British species the body length of adults may be as small as 15mm (*Dendrobaena pygmaea* (p. 73)) or as large as 300mm (*L. terrestris*) and the diameter varies correspondingly from 1 to 10 mm. External transverse grooves, or **furrows**, mark the positions of the internal **septa** that divide the body into a linear series of similar compartments, **somites** or **metameres**, the primary **segments**. Externally secondary furrows, **annuli**, are often present, the triannulate condition being common. The first body segment, the **peristomium**, surrounds the mouth and dorsally carries a forwardly directed fleshy lobe, the **prostomium** (Fig. 1). When the worm is at rest, the prostomium acts as a flap and seals the entrance to the mouth or **buccal cavity** but otherwise it is employed as a tactile and chemo-sensory probe; in *Lumbricus* spp. it is additionally prehensile and used to draw grasses and leaves into the burrow. The prostomium may be continuous posteriorly with the peristomium, **zygolobous**; have a simple demarcation, **prolobous**; have a short posterior tongue-like projection, **epilobous**, or have the tongue-like projection extend back to the first furrow and divide the peristomium dorsally, **tanylobous** (Fig. 2). Posteriorly the last segment of the body is the anal segment or **periproct** with a small median opening, the **anus**, usually seen as a short vertical slit. The numbers of segments are fairly constant within each species, the more so in small populations, but there are some variations, e.g. 83–100 (*Satchellius mammalis* (p. 118)) to 86–255 (*Eisenia veneta* (p. 88). Most young worms possess the definitive adult number of segments for the species when they emerge from their egg-capsules and any subsequent additions are replacements by regeneration following injury or caudal autonomy. With the exceptions of the peristomium and the periproct which are non-setigerous, retractile **setae*** are

*We follow Brinkhurst, R. O. ('British and other marine and estuarine oligochaetes.' *Synopses of the British Fauna* (New Series) No. 21, 1982) in using the widely known word "seta" from *saeta* (Latin) = bristle, for a chitinous bristle in the body wall of an earthworm, instead of the alternative term "chaeta". Usage of the established class name 'Oligochaeta' is a separate matter since the compound word is a proper noun, albeit with Greek stems, employed as a higher group name in zoological nomenclature. (See *seta* in the Glossary.)

4

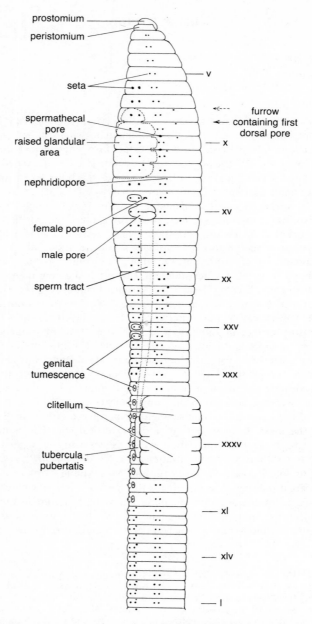

prostomium

peristomium

seta

v

furrow
containing first
dorsal pore

spermathecal
pore

raised glandular
area

x

nephridiopore

xv

female pore

male pore

sperm tract

xx

xxv

genital
tumescence

xxx

clitellum

xxxv

tubercula
pubertatis

xl

xlv

l

Fig. 1. *Lumbricus terrestris*. External morphology, left lateral of the anterior region.
Roman numerals denote segment numbers.

5

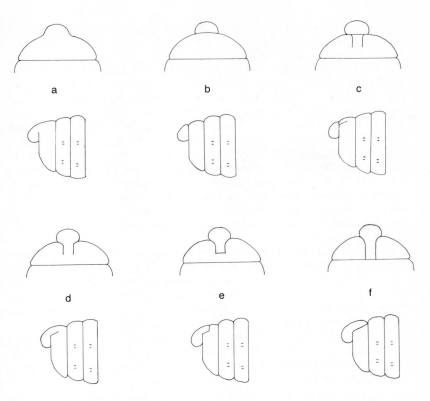

Fig. 2. Morphology of the prostomium. dorsal (upper rows) and left lateral views (lower rows). (*a*) zygolobous, (*b*) prolobous, (*c*) proepilobous i.e. combined pro- and epilobous, (*d*) epilobous (open), (*e*) epilobous (closed) and (*f*) tanylobous.

present on every segment of the body. Most earthworms have eight (four pairs) of setae located ventrally and lateroventrally on each segment, the **lumbricine** (sometimes *octochaetine*) arrangement, but a few tropical genera have numerous setae, 40–200, distributed around the equator of each segment, the **perichaetine** arrangement (Fig. 7). The setae are sigmoid in shape with a median nodule into which retractor muscles are inserted. They vary in size among species, members of the same species and along the body of an individual where the setae in the anterior and posterior regions are often enlarged for use in locomotion. Some ventral pairs may be modified as genital setae and carried singly or as couples on low glandular, papilliform pads, the **genital tumescences.** Under a microscope these setae are seen to have a longitudinal groove and may be hooked distally. Their function is possibly for tactile stimulation and holding a partner during **copulation.** Paired **penial setae** occurring either singly or in bundles of several setae are additionally present by the prostatic pores of some Megascolecoidea. They are usually ornamented characteristically according to species and frequently are much longer than the ordinary setae.

A small intersegmental opening, the **dorsal pore**, is present mid-dorsally in all but the anterior furrows of the bodies of some earthworms families including the Lumbricidae. Each pore perforates the body wall to lead into the large body cavity or **coelom**. It is controlled by a sphincter muscle which permits the coelomic fluid to exude over the cuticle to help moisten and protect the body surface. The coelomic fluid may be vigorously expelled in response to chemical irritation or, in a few species, attack by a predator. In the Lumbricidae and most other families, osmo-regulatory and other excretory products are discharged through a pair of inconspicuous lateral pores, the **nephridiopores**, present in the hinder wall of every furrow except for a few in the anterior region. These pores usually form a continuous row along the body slightly above the ventral setal couple but occasionally they are irregularly arranged.

Earthworms are **hermaphrodite** with each individual having both male and female reproductive systems, mostly restricted to only a few anterior segments. Usually a single pair of **male pores** are present between the two setal couples on or behind segment *xiii*, in the case of the family Lumbricidae mainly on segment *xv*. The male pores are commonly small, even inconspicuous, but some Lumbricidae have large male pores with tumid lips, or **tumescences**. The **female pores** are minute on segment *xiv* and usually paired lateroventrally. The pores of paired flask-like invaginations of the body wall for storing received sperm, the **spermathecae**, are present anteriorly in most earthworms. In British species paired spermathecal pores are present in several anterior furrows especially between segments *ix, x* and *xi*. They are commonly at the level of the lateral setal couple but occasionally are located more dorsally (Fig. 1).

A glandular swelling, the **clitellum** (sometimes known as the girdle, saddle or *cingulum* = 'belt') develops over several segments in the anterior half of the body of the adults. Here the **epidermis** becomes modified with the presence of numerous large gland cells that produce a mucoid secretion which forms a mucus filled slime tube, cocoon or **egg capsule** for the nourishment and protection of the developing embryos. The position and number of segments modified to form the clitellum are nearly constant in each species. In the Lumbricidae the clitellum is usually **saddle-shaped** or incomplete ventrally, extending from the dorsum to beyond the lateral setal couple; less often it is **annular** or complete ventrally to form a tube or ring-like belt. The swelling is frequently sufficient to obliterate the intersegmental furrows, the dorsal pores and either or both the lateral and ventral setal couples depending on whether it is saddle-shaped or annular. Specializations develop along the ventral margins of saddle-shaped clitella of non-Megascolecoid species; here glandular ridges or grooves develop, often intersected by intersegmental furrows, or discrete segmental papillae arise to form the

tubercula pubertatis (tubercles of 'puberty'). The number of segments bearing tubercula pubertatis seldom varies within a species. The tubercula pubertatis apparently function during mating for they are sometimes absent from individuals reproducing by **parthenogenesis**, i.e. asexually. They may appear before the clitellum reaches its full development so permitting aclitellate adolescent worms to copulate with sexually mature worms and exchange spermatozoa while yet unable to produce egg capsules.

The **body wall** consists of an outer cuticle, the glandular epidermis, the dermis, circular and longitudinal muscle layers separated by a thin network of nervous tissue and, finally, the peritoneum lining the coelomic cavity (Fig. 3). The **cuticle** is non-cellular and although thin and transparent, it is tough and covers all of the body except where it is perforated by the setae and/or glandular and other pores. Light is refracted as it passes through the cuticle and affects the perceived colour of the underlying body wall and gives an iridescence. The **epidermis** consists, except on the clitellum, of a single layer of cells elongated vertically; many of these cells have the character of unicellular glands, many others are sensory cells being connected by fine nerve fibres with the nerve cord. Below the epidermis is a layer of connective

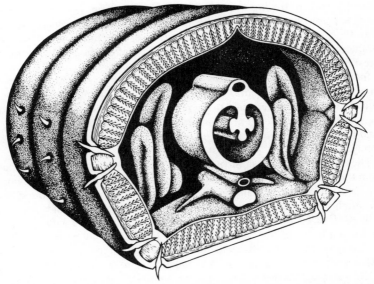

Fig. 3. *Lumbricus sp.* Schematic diagram of a transverse section through the intestinal region showing the outer circular and inner (pennate) longitudinal muscles of the body wall and the arrangement of the setae. The intestine is shown with an internal mid-dorsal typhlosole and externally with the dorsal blood vessel above and the ventral vessel below; the ventral nerve cord lies on the mid-ventral parietes and paired nephidia are shown laterally to the intestine. (© *British Museum (Natural History)*, 1975).

tissue, the **dermis**, surrounding the muscles of the body wall. The outer layer, the **circular muscle**, is thin whereas the underlying layer of **longitudinal muscle** is, by comparison, massive. The structure of the longitudinal muscles of most British earthworms is **pennate** ('feather-like') but it is **intermediate** in *Aporrectodea icterica* (p. 58), **radiate** in *Allolobophora chlorotica* (p. 50) and **simple** in the introduced exotic, *Microscolex phosphoreus* (p. 140). Other muscle types have been described from elsewhere, e.g. France (*see* Bouché, 1972:72 for an account of the structures of longitudinal muscles). Body colour is fundamentally dependent upon the presence or absence of pigment in these muscles. Earthworms have the red respiratory pigment **haemoglobin** in solution in their blood that gives them a basic 'flesh' colour (Laverack, 1963). Many have additional pigments, mainly **porphyrins**, thought to be the by-products of metabolism. Some species (*Lumbricus* (p. 96)) have a red/purple pigment but due to the optical effect of the cuticle, violet and deep blue hues are frequently seen especially dorsally where the pigmentation is more intense. Others (*Aporrectodea*), have a brown/black pigment, **melanin**, producing golden brown or greenish tints. Occasionally pigmentation may be restricted to a transverse stripe on each segment without pigment in the intervening furrow so giving the worm a banded appearance (*Eisenia fetida* (p. 80)). In the intestinal region colours can often be seen through the body wall especially the yellow pigment of peritoneal **chlorogogenous cells** over the intestine. These cells are concerned with the removal of waste products. The colour of the ingested soil can also affect the body colour in the intestinal region.

Internally throughout the body, the body segments are separated from one another by a series of septa. A septum consists of two layers of peritoneal cells which enclose between them muscular fibres, connective tissue and blood vessels. Most septa are thin and delicate but anteriorly in the region used for active burrowing, some, according to species, may be thickened and highly muscular.

The digestive tract or **alimentary canal** passes without any coiling straight from the mouth to the terminal **anus** (Fig. 4). In the first four body segments it is differentiated into a **pharynx** from whence the **oesophagus** extends back for another nine to thirteen or so segments to the beginning of the **intestine** (Fig. 4). **Calciferous glands** or **Glands of Morren**, concerned with the control of calcium levels of the blood (Laverack, 1963:24), may be present on the oesophagus. In the Lumbricidae uniquely they form a swollen region in the mid-oesophagus; on dissection, they can be seen to consist of a series of folds in the inner wall of the oesophagus, **intra-mural**, discharging into the lumen in segment x or xi. When they occur in other families, the calciferous glands are **extra-mural** comprising one or more pairs of (often stalked lamellate) glands arising dorso-laterally from the external wall of the posterior region of the oesophagus. Oesophageal **gizzards** are present in most families of earthworms but absent from the Lumbricidae where instead the anterior end of the intestine is modified to form a **crop** followed by a muscular gizzard;

9

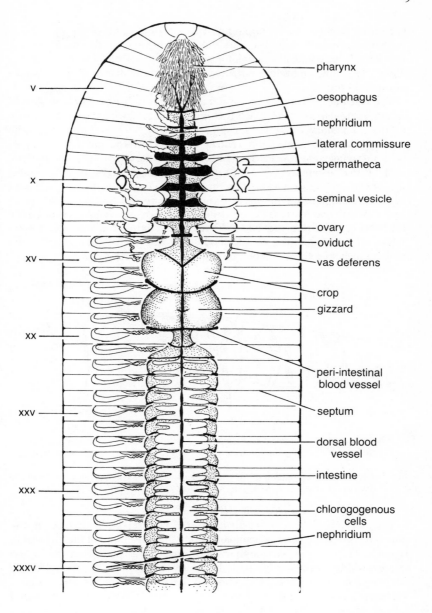

Fig. 4. *Lumbricus terrestris*. Internal morphology, general dissection of the anterior region, dorsal view. (Nephridia *not* shown on the right side.) Roman numerals denote segment numbers.

each usually one segment in length. The anterior region of the intestine is further specialized with the internal development of the **typhlosole**, a mid-dorsal, longitudinal evagination or downfold, often filling much of the lumen, providing additional surface area for the assimilation of the products of digested food.

The **vascular system** is closed. There are three main trunks or blood vessels: a contractile **dorsal vessel** which is closely associated with the dorsal surface of the alimentary canal for most of its length, and two non-contractile ventrally located trunks, the **ventral vessel** below the gut and a largely post-oesophageal **subneural vessel** between the nerve cord and the parietal wall. In the oesophageal region, segmentally paired lateral vessels connect the dorsal and ventral vessels from segment *vi* to *xi* to form a series of strongly enlarged and muscular **commissural vessels** that since the more posterior pairs, at least, are contractile, are known as **pseudohearts** or **lateral hearts** (Fig. 5). From segment *xii* backwards, peri-oesophageal then peri-intestinal vessels join the dorsal blood vessel with the sub-neural vessel and may be mistaken for a homologue of the lateral hearts.

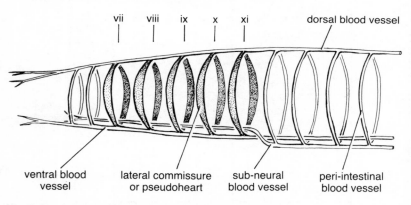

Fig. 5. *Lumbricus sp.* Diagram of the major blood vessels of the anterior region of the body. Roman numerals denote segment numbers.

The nervous system of earthworms follows the basic pattern of the annelids. A bilobed **cerebral ganglion** lies on the dorsal wall of the pharynx in segment *iii*, a pair of **circumpharyngeal connectives** pass from the lateral borders of the ganglion around the pharynx and unite ventrally in the **suboesophageal ganglion** in segment *iv*. The ventral nerve cord extends backwards from the union of the two circumpharyngeal connectives and passes throughout the remainder of the body as two halves fused together swelling slightly in each segment to form a **ganglion**. In a typical segment, three pairs of trunks pass laterally, one anteriorly from the ventral nerve cord and two from the ganglion. A segmental nervous system comprises mainly a nerve ring, incomplete dorsally, lying mostly between the circular and longitudinal muscle layers.

The **excretory system** is usually composed of a single pair of coiled **nephridia** in each segment except often the first three segments and the periproct. These large nephridia are known as **meganephridia** or **holonephridia**. Each meganephridium has a funnel-like **nephrostome** that opens in the preceding segment and leads into a coiled tube with a small diameter that increases in size to form, in most species, a bladder-like **nephridial vesicle** before opening onto the body surface by an inconspicuous **nephridiopore** (Edwards and Lofty, 1977:29). Each meganephridium is served by **afferent** and **efferent blood vessels** from the ventral and dorsal blood vessels respectively, thus it is able to perform an excretory function and maintain an osmo-regulatory/ionic balance in the blood. The shape of the nephridial vesicle varies according to the species and its ecology. Among the Lumbricidae, unspecialized species such as *Helodrilus oculatus* lack nephridial vesicles and the worms are confined permanently to moist soils; *Eisenia* (p. 79), *Eiseniella* (p. 90) and *Dendrobaena* (p. 68) possess sausage- to ocarina-shaped, globular (sacciform) vesicles and are unable to survive in dry soils while most soil-dwelling earthworms such as species of *Lumbricus* (p. 96), *Aporrectodea* (p. 53) etc. have elongate, tubular vesicles (uncinate, U-shaped or fish-hook shaped) which enable the rate of water loss to be controlled not only during daily life in the soil but also during drought. (For an account of the nephridial vesicles in the family Lumbricidae, *see* Perel, 1976.) The excretory systems of some Megascolecoidea are different with the single pair of meganephrida replaced in each segment by numerous small **micronephridia** or **meronephridia**. These micronephridia are variable in structure and may discharge directly onto the body surface or through intersegmental ducts that may open either externally or discharge into the intestine.

The **male reproductive system** comprises paired testes in each of segments *x* and *xi* (**holandry**) these are attached to the anterior septum close to the nerve cord. Some exotic species have paired testes in segment *x* only (**proandry**), others in *xi* only (**metandry**). In most genera the testes are 'free', i.e. not enclosed by testis sacs, so the sperm material fills most of the coelomic cavity of the testes segments. In all species there are sperm storage sacs, the **seminal vesicles**, seen as posteriorly directed pouches formed from the hinder septum of each testes segment and filling much of the available space in the next segment, i.e. in segments *xi* and/or *xii*. In *Lumbricus* (p. 96) and some other genera the testes are enclosed by **testis sacs**, these develop characteristically in association with the seminal vesicles which they resemble and have an analogous function (Fig. 6). Thus *Octolasion* (p. 112) species are described as having four pairs of seminal vesicles, one pair in each of segments *ix*, *x*, *xi* and *xii* and *Lumbricus* species, three pairs in segments *ix*, *xi* and *xii*. Paired sperm ducts, **vasa deferentia** (singular *vas deferens*), with ental funnels for the collection of the sperm, pass posteriorly from each testes

12

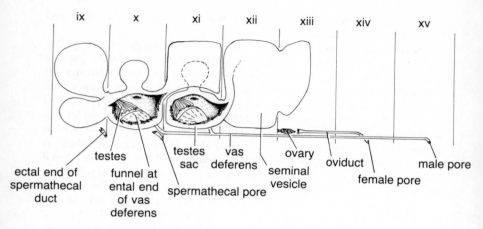

ix   x   xi   xii   xiii   xiv   xv

testes

testes   vas
sac   deferens

ovary
seminal
vesicle

oviduct

male pore

ectal end of
spermathecal
duct

funnel at
ental end
of vas
deferens

spermathecal pore

female pore

Fig. 6. *Lumbricus terrestris*. Schematic diagram of the male and female reproductive systems of the left side. Left lateral view with contents of the testes sacs displayed and the spermathecae removed. Roman numerals denote segment numbers.

segment. In holandric species, those on each side unite to form a single (paired) duct that leads to the male pore. The vasa deferentia are modified in a few species (*Aporrectodea* (p. 53)); after passing back through the septum into the segment containing the seminal vesicle, each becomes highly convoluted to form a coiled mass of unknown function, the **epididymus**. In the megascolecoid subfamily Eudrilinae (p. 145), the funnels at the (ental) ends of the vasa deferentia are continuous with the seminal vesicles and enclose the testes to form subterminal **sperm reservoirs**. In (exotic) proandric species, there is a single pair of seminal vesicles in segment *xi* while metandric species have a single pair or seminal vesicles in segment *xii*. The seminal vesicles of metandric species are occasionally long and may pass posteriorly through twenty or more segments while their anterior regions may be reduced to slender ducts, e.g. *Polytoreutus* (Sims, 1982*a*). Accessory male glands are absent from the Lumbricidae but prostate-like glands (not associated with the male pores) are present in other lumbricoid and some glossoscolecoid families; true **prostates** (associated with the male pore(s)) are present mainly in megascolecoid species.

The **female reproductive system** comprises a pair of **ovaries** pendent from the hinder surface of the anterior septum of segment *xiii* near the ventral parietes by the nerve cord. The structure varies according to the superfamily (Sims, 1980) but in the Lumbricidae, each ovary is discoidal with the budding **oöcytes** forming a single string. **Ova** are shed into the coelomic fluid where they are taken up by the **fimbriated funnels** at the ental ends of the short, paired **oviducts** that lead to the exterior through the female pores on the next segment. Flask-like containers, the **spermathecae**, store sperm received from a concopulant during mating (Fig. 6). In the Lumbricidae they are small and paired, usually located in several pre-testicular segments, sometimes partly or wholly within the body wall. The spermathecae are mostly simple in structure with a proximal stem or **duct** and a distal sac-like **ampulla**, in megascolecoid species the spermathecae are larger and often have a single **diverticulum** (rarely more) arising from the duct. Spermathecae are absent from a few species that transfer sperm in capsule-like structures, the **spermatophores**, or where the ovum develops into a juvenile without the union with a **spermatozoön, parthenogenesis.** Spermathecae have been replaced in the family Eudrilidae mostly by a post-testicular system of coelomic sacs and ducts that lead from the 'spermathecal' pore(s) to communicate with the oviducts.

Two conventions are followed in the description of earthworms. The first concerns the identification of the numerous segments and furrows. To prevent confusion, the numbers of the segments are recorded as roman numerals when the word 'segment' is commonly omitted, e.g. the location of the male pore on the fifteenth segment is written as 'male pore, *xv*'. (Note that the roman numeral is printed in lower case italic type to avoid confusion with any other abbreviations that may be used.) Furrows, however, are denoted by the arabic numerals of the segments on either side, thus the furrow forming the posterior boundary to the segment bearing the male pore, i.e. *xv*, is '15/16'. The second convention concerns the identification of the setae. In each species the relative distances between the setae are fairly constant throughout the body with the exception of the anterior region. As they are taxonomically important, setal distances need to be measured (usually in the segments immediately behind the clitellum). The setal pairs of each segment are designated by the letters *a, b, c* and *d* beginning with the ventralmost pair. When the distances between setae *ab* and between *cd* are small, the setae are termed as 'closely paired', as the distances increase they are termed as 'widely paired' and finally when *a, b, c* and *d* approach equi-distance, they are termed as 'distant' (Fig. 7). The relative distances between the setae are usually expressed more precisely, in the older literature as an

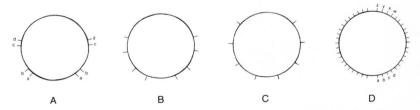

Fig. 7. Arrangement of the setae of earthworms. (*A–C*) Lumbricine or octochaetine arrangement with four pairs per segment; the setae are designated *a, b, c, d* on each side as shown. (*A*) closely paired (*B*) widely paired and (*C*) distant. (*D*) Perichaetine arrangement of setae, setae numerous; setae are designated *a, b, c, d* . . . on each side beginning from the mid-ventral line and *z, y, x, w* . . . on each side beginning from the mid-dorsal line.

equation ($aa = 4cd$, $ab > cd$, $aa = bc + cd$) but nowadays usually as ratios ($aa : ab : bc : cd : dd$). Unfortunately there is no agreement among zoologists about the methods of assessing the ratios, some measure the distances with fine-pointed calipers or through the graticule eyepiece in a microscope while others attempt to express the intervals as percentages of the total circumference. For convenience in this guide, the smallest distance, usually cd, is expressed as unity and all other distances as a multiple. The dorsal distance is frequently given as a fraction of the circumference and readily expresses the general situation of the setae, e.g. '$dd = \frac{3}{4}$ circumference' indicates that all of the setae, are situated ventrally. (In some books the circumference is indicated by the letter u, an abbreviation of the German word *Umkreis* = "circumference".) In large species these intervals can be measured direct but in small species or softened specimens the best method is to cut out a small section of the body wall, open it along the dorsal line, remove the intestine then flatten the body wall before taking the measurements. The setal ratios are constant among conspecific series that have received comparable treatments during collection and storage. However, by subjecting specimens of a single species (especially those of varying sizes) to differing techniques for relaxing, fixing and preserving, variations can be produced in the setal ratios of greater magnitude than the differences between closely allied species. The reason for these discrepancies appears to lie in the non-uniformity of the thickness of the longitudinal muscles around the body, in particular along the setal lines where the muscles are reduced. Depending on the treatment received, the contractions of the longitudinal and opposing circular muscles can vary to affect the inter-setal distances. Nevertheless this variation is insufficient to affect the overall usefulness of setal distance as a taxonomic character (also for describing the location of pores relative to the setal lines.)

Biology

General

The sub-order Lumbricina contains 24 families and sub-families of earthworms occuring in various parts of the world (Sims, 1980). The great majority of species are highly adapted both morphologically and physiologically to their environments and cannot withstand transference to different conditions. Their food preferences together with narrow temperature, humidity and pH tolerances not only restrict their ranges but also contribute towards the overall dissimilarities and uniqueness of species. These differences are sufficient to prevent all but the general principles of biology to be applied to all members of the sub-order (Edwards and Lofty, 1977; Wallwork, 1983). Unfortunately misconceptions are widespread often due to fallacious assumptions of the validity of the general application of information derived from laboratory studies, mostly on the specialized boreal species *Eisenia fetida* (p. 80), a manure worm, and *Lumbricus terrestris* (p. 106) that forages at night on the surface of the soil and constructs deep, permanent burrows in the soil.

Reproduction and life history

All earthworms are hermaphrodite and as their reproductive systems are similar, testes paired in segments *x* and/or *xi* and the ovaries paired in segment *xiii* their breeding behaviours are essentially alike. Reproduction usually begins with a mutual interchange of spermatozoa during copulation between two individuals. The received spermatozoa are stored in the spermathecae (or in analagous structures in the African family Eudrilidae) where their presence may be detected by an iridescence, even in preserved specimens. Fertilization of the ova occurs later, perhaps after several days, within an egg-capsule produced to protect and nourish the developing embryos.

Copulation is generally accomplished by two individuals coming to lie 'head-to-tail' so that the clitellar region of each is tightly applied to the body wall in the spermathecal region of the other. The clitellum is often broad and during copulation can almost encircle the body of a concopulant, especially in species with dorsally located spermathecal pores, e.g. *Eisenia fetida* (Fig. 8). In species of families without prostates or prostate-like glands, copious mucus is secreted by the clitellum; as the outer surface of the mucus dries, it tightly encloses the clitellar region of a concopulant with the spermathecal region of its partner while the sperm are transferred safely in the fluid medium. The importance of the clitellum during copulation is reduced in

16

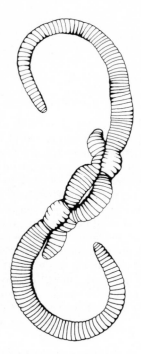

Fig. 8. *Eisenia fetida*. Two individuals mating. (© *British Museum* (*Natural History*), 1975).

families that possess glandular prostates, such as members of the Megascolecoidea; in the case of most worms in the huge *Pheretima*-group the clitellum is annular and extends for only three segments. In these worms, sperm material is carried in the fluid produced by the prostates and as the combined male and prostatic pores (sometimes eversible) are exactly the same distance apart as the spermathecal pores, the sperm are transferred directly into the spermathecae.

Mating pairs of *Lumbricus terrestris* always copulate on the surface of the soil, usually at night, whereas other British species almost invariably couple below the surface. Copulation may last for $\frac{1}{2}$–4 hours. Afterwards some species may carry a few small spermatophores, producing or containing spermatozoa, loosely attached ventrally on the segments around the male pores or in the clitellar region. (The spermatophores vary according to species and usually become detached, falling off during preservation.) The spermatophores may act as substitutes for the spermathecae in species lacking these organs (Bouché, 1975). Each is probably formed from a diploid spermatogonium which undergoes repeated cell division eventually to provide the haploid spermatozoa for the fertilization of the ova. Copulation may occur several times a year and has been reported between parthenogenetic, i.e. functionally female, adults also between individuals of different species, e.g. *Lumbricus terrestris* (p. 106) and *L. festivus* (p. 100). Mating appears to stimulate the release of ova since mated worms usually produce egg-capsules at a much higher rate than unmated worms.

Many species reproduce without mating, either by self-fertilization or parthenogenesis, when external secondary characters such as the tubercula pubertatis may fail to develop (Hartenstein, Neuhauser and Easton, 1980). In Britain, these species include *Aporrectodea rosea* (p. 65), *Dendrobaena octaedra* (p. 72), *Dendrodrilus rubidus* (p. 76), *Eisenia fetida* (p. 80), *Eiseniella tetraedra* (p. 90), *Lumbricus eiseni* (p. 98), *Murchieona minuscula* (p. 109), *Octolasion cyaneum* (p. 112), *O. tyrtaeum* (p. 115), and *Satchellius mammalis* (p. 118). However, self-propagation is limited and when unmated individuals of other species are kept in isolation, embryos may fail to develop within the egg-capsules (*Lumbricus* spp.) or egg-capsules may not even be produced (*Aporrectodea* spp.). Most lumbricid worms come slowly into breeding condition with the clitellum gradually changing colour from pink to orange then brown before finally turning white when the highly glandular epidermis swells to its maximum size. This hypertrophy of the clitellum regresses only after an egg-capsule has been produced, then the region reverts to the same colour and diameter as the surrounding segments and the intersegmental furrows re-appear. When the worm is about to lay its eggs, the clitellum produces a slime-tube or band that dries somewhat externally and fills with an albuminous fluid. The band is moved forwards by peristaltic movements of the body and ova are discharged into it as it passes over the female pores. Then when it reaches the spermathecal pores, received sperm are emitted and fertilization takes place. The band continues forward until it is released over the anterior end of the body to form a spherical to ovoid egg-capsule (or oöphore) with short, polar tuft-like projections as the open ends of the band close-up (Fig. 9). At first the outer membrane of the capsule is usually thin and transparent but it soon becomes translucent and yellowish-green to brown in colour while the albuminous liquid contents may be either translucent or opaque. In several *Lumbricus* spp., the outer membrane becomes opaque, tough and multi-layered. A capsule may contain up to 20 eggs but it is unusual for more than one to undergo full development and hatch.

Locomotion and movement

Locomotion is produced by the co-ordinated action of the outer, circular body wall muscles and the inner, opposing longitudinal muscles ennervated by segmental nerves acting on the coelomic fluid. When the circular muscles contract they cause segments to become more slender. Because liquids are incompressible, the volume of the coelomic fluid is maintained so the length of the segment increases. In contrast, when the longitudinal muscles

18

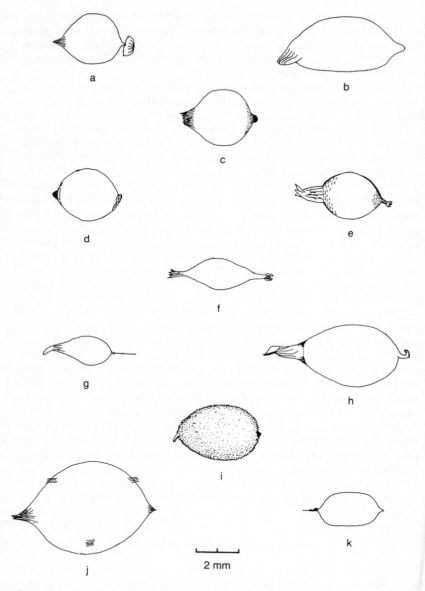

Fig. 9. Egg capsules. (*a*) *Allobophora chlorotica*, (*b*) *Aporrectodea longa*, (*c*) *Aporrectodea rosea*, (*d*) *Dendrobaena octaedra*, (*e*) *Dendrodrilus rubidus*, (*f*) *Eisenia fetida*, (*g*) *Eiseniella tetraedra*, (*h*) *Lumbricus eiseni*, (*i*) *Lumbricus rubellus*, (*j*) *Lumbricus terrestris* and (*k*) *Octolasion cyaneum* (after Evans and Guild, 1948; Svendsen, 1956 and Gerard, 1964).

contract, they produce a shortening of the segments which become correspondingly stouter. Thus the coelomic fluid by maintaining its volume, facilitates the interactions of the opposing sets of muscles and functions as an internal, **hydrostatic skeleton** (Clark, 1981). When the anterior region is thrust forwards, the internal pressure in the fore body is considerable, over $70\,\text{gf/cm}^2$ (1 lb per square inch) have been measured in the coelomic fluid of *Lumbricus terrestris*.

Forward movement is achieved by setae on the mid-body segments being raised by the contractions of their small muscles so causing them to grip the substratum. At the same time a wave of contractions of the circular muscles passes back along the body causing the anterior region to lengthen and to be thrust forward. When the circular muscles of this region reach their maximum contractions, the setae of the region are raised to grip the substrate as a backward wave of contractions of the longitudinal muscles produces a shortening of the segments of the anterior end. This has the affect of drawing-up the hinder parts of the body where meanwhile the setal muscles have relaxed and the setae released their anchorage to permit the region to move forward (Fig. 10). As the complex cycles may be synchronized with similar cycles replicated simultaneously along the body, the total effect can be a rippling, flowing, forward movement. Details of locomotion vary according to the size of an individual and the extent to which each species is adapted to life in its own particular environment (Piearce, 1983).

Burrows are constructed in loose soil usually by the worm extending the anterior end of the body (circular muscles contracted) while using the prostomium to probe between soil particles to produce a small diameter tunnel. Next the setae in this region grip the walls of the narrow-bore tunnel and the longitudinal muscles of the anterior region contract causing the body diameter to increase considerably and enlarge the narrow tunnel into a burrow. The actions of a worm compact together the particles to give a structural stability to the burrow while mucus secreted by the glandular epidermal cells cement together the particles giving it a durable lining. The muscles of the body wall in the anterior region of most earthworms are thickened to produce the strength necessary to construct burrows while the internal septa in this region are commonly highly muscularized to withstand comparatively high internal pressures. Further morphological adaptation to high pressure in powerfully burrowing species is seen in the location of the first dorsal pore. In these species it occurs posteriorly behind the region of high pressure, in furrow 12/13 in *Aporrectodea longa* (p. 62) whereas in the non-burrowing, litter-dwelling species without muscularized anterior septa, there is no region of high pressure and the first dorsal pore occurs more anteriorly, in furrow 5/6 in the case of *Dendrodrilus rubidus* (p. 76).

Deep, permanent vertical burrows that open at the soil surface are made mainly by large species such as *Aporrectodea "nocturna"* (p. 57), *A. longa* (p. 62), *Lumbricus friendi* (p. 102) and *L. terrestris* (p. 106) by pushing aside soil particles then compacting the soil, whereas shallow temporary horizontal

20

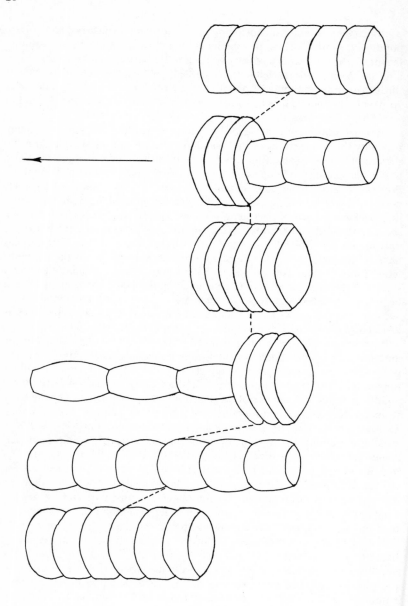

Fig. 10. Hydrostatic skeleton. Diagram illustrates the effects of cycles of muscular contractions causing changes in the proportions of the segments during locomotion. Throughout these cycles the volume of each segment remains constant.

burrows are produced by geophagous species such as *Octolasion* spp (p. 112), that seldom emerge onto the surface and in heavy soils almost literally eat their way through the ground. Surface browsing species such as *Lumbricus terrestris* need to move to the surface to obtain food (leaves, blades of grass etc. which are drawn back into the burrow for consumption in safety) and also to breed. During these activities the depressed, paddle-shaped posterior region of the body often remains within the opening to the burrow acting as a holdfast and so facilitating a rapid withdrawal in case of danger. The most mobile group of species in Britain, the small red-pigmented worms, do not burrow but instead live in small crevices, on the surface of the ground in litter, under stones, moss or the bark of fallen trees and move freely in search of food.

Feeding

Most earthworms are omnivorous, deriving their nutrition from organic matter in the form of living plant material (roots, leaves, seedlings and seeds of angiosperms), decomposing remains of plants (dead roots, lawn clippings, freshly fallen leaves and leaf litter), microscopic animals (protozoa, nematode larvae, acari and collembola), the faeces of large animals especially herbivores, as well as bacteria, yeasts and fungi. The food is usually ingested with soil which together pass through the alimentary canal. Earthworms possess many digestive enzymes, including cellulases and chitinases, but also benefit from a symbiotic relationship with intestinal micro-organisms. The numbers of micro-organisms taken in with soil and organic matter is high; most yeasts and other species lacking a protective coat are readily digested but some bacteria and actinomycete fungi survive and may multiply up to a thousand-fold during passage through the alimentary canal. The feeding rate of *Lumbricus terrestris* (p. 106), for example, increases in the presence of the bacterium *Pseudomonas aeruginosa* while certain species of mobile protozoa may be essential for normal growth in *Eisenia fetida* (p. 80) since life cannot be sustained in their absence (*see* Parasites).

A number of species are selective feeders, in Britain usually the red-pigmented earthworms that live in forest litter, under leaf compost or dung-pats, or, in the case of the large *Lumbricus* spp., that browse on surface vegetation. Species of *Lumbricus* have a long, almost proboscis-like, tanylobic prostomium that enables them to grasp an object by holding it against the upper lip or 'roof' of the mouth. This ability permits surface browsing and enables these worms to pull food from the surface into the burrow for storage and later consumption in safety. Small seedlings may be uprooted by *Lumbricus terrestris* and this same species will also reach up to the lower leaves of small plants to indulge in extracellular digestion whilst the former are still firmly attached to the plant. The pharynx is everted, digestive fluids are poured onto the leaf and the softened tissues consumed. This action produces the condition well-known to gardeners of bedding plants losing their leaf tips.

Earthworms generally are detritivores, some being secondary decomposers of plant material and others, the selective feeders, whose gut contents consist primarily of organic fragments, being primary decomposers. The latter are largely responsible for casting organic fragments into undisturbed (unploughed) subsoil, an essential phase in soil production (Satchell, 1983).

Growth

Several hours, or days, may elapse between an earthworm shedding each of its egg-capsules, which are found scattered in the soil predominantly in the layers of soil or litter layer commonly inhabited by the adults. Those in the top layers are subjected to the greatest diurnal and seasonal variations in both temperature and soil humidity pF (water potential). Embryonic development is arrested immediately when capsules of *Allolobophora chlorotica* (p. 50) and *Aporrectodea caliginosa* (p. 54) are subjected to low temperatures (5°C and below) and within a few days when they are transferred to very dry soils (pF 4.44); nevertheless, under either of these conditions, the embryos can remain unharmed in a state of quiescence for several weeks. When there is adequate water, juveniles may emerge from the egg-capsules of *Allolobophora chlorotica* after 36 days at 20°C, 52 days at 15°C and 119 days at 10°C. Egg-capsules laid when the temperatures are falling in the autumn, develop slowly and fully formed juveniles do not hatch until a suitable temperature threshold is attained in the spring, usually in May when large numbers of juveniles emerge simultaneously. (Newly hatched juveniles living in the loose surface layers of the soil are susceptible to predation of starlings, rooks and other shallow-probing birds and when the top soil layers dry out, to desiccation as unlike adult worms they are too weak to burrow into deeper layers.) Under favourable temperatures and with adequate food, e.g. in laboratory cultures, juveniles will grow rapidly into clitellate adults; both *Allolobophora chlorotica* and *Aporrectodea caliginosa* take 17 to 19 weeks at 15°C (Graff, 1953; Edwards and Lofty, 1977) and *Eisenia fetida* (p. 80) only 51.5 days at 25°C (Tomlin and Miller, 1980). However in naturally fluctuating conditions, *Lumbricus terrestris* probably takes three to four years to mature but this slow growing species is long-lived with adults surviving in cultures for up to thirty years. The natural longevity of most earthworms is short with small species unlikely to survive the hazards in natural habitats for more than $1\frac{1}{2}$ years.

Increase in weight is greatest during autumn and spring with weight being lost during the winter and summer when worms 'hibernate' and 'aestivate'. The overall weight of *Lumbricus terrestris* increases over the first 3–5 years to 8–12 g in grassland soils and occasionally 15–18 g when food is especially rich and abundant, as in compost heaps. Then the contents of the alimentary canal may weigh as much as 20% of the live weight (95% of the weight of earthworm tissues being water).

The mean number of segments is characteristic for each species but the actual number per individual varies from one series to another. This variation is produced largely by differing physical conditions affecting the development of the embryos and juveniles in one place at a given time compared with another place or time. Generally the young of large adults (producing large egg-capsules with an abundance of 'rich' albuminous nourishment) and developing under favourable conditions of temperature and humidity, are more likely to achieve the maximum numbers of segments for the species than the young developed in little albuminous fluid during a cold, dry growing season.

Many species emerge from the egg-capsules with the adult number of segments and during their first season before the winter quiescence, increase only their linear dimensions. Juveniles of other species, for example *Eisenia fetida* and *E. veneta*, emerge from their egg-capsules with fewer segments than the adults and increase not only their linear dimensions but also their number of body segments during the season after hatching. In these species the final number of segments is dependent not only on soil temperatures and humidities but also the duration between hatching and 'hibernation'. Thus the earlier that a worm hatches, the longer is the growth period and the greater the number of segments produced (Mazantseva, 1982). Local fluctuations in physical conditions (which also affect food supply) produce variations that prevent the establishment of growth coefficients. Nevertheless, individuals of the same age and species from the same sample exhibit little variation in segment number. This growth phase ceases with the fall in temperatures in the autumn and the onset of quiescence. With the resumption of activity in the following spring, the worms mature with the body metabolism converting energy mainly into sexual products.

Regeneration

Earthworms possess the ability to replicate segments but the extent to which damaged or lost segments can be replaced varies according to species and in the case of loss, the region of the body. Caudal regeneration is common not only among members of the family Lumbricidae but also in the members of all earthworm families; further the number of segments lost is largely characteristic for each species. Since this widespread phenomenon is found even in populations in primary tropical grasslands and forests, it cannot be attributed to damage by farming equipment or predators such as the European mole, *Talpa europea*. (Birds cannot be connected with caudal amputation since they sieze earthworms by the head region which would be consumed even if a worm were broken and the posterior region remained in the burrow.) Semal-van Gansen (1956) showed that caudal autotomy, a spontaneous shedding of the posterior region, occurs in adults of *Eisenia fetida* when the caudal region reaches a threshold and cannot accumulate further insoluble waste in the coelom. The use of the caudal region for refuse may often be observed in other species when the posterior segments are brightly coloured by pigments from the waste products of nitrogen metabolism.

Caudal autotomy followed by regeneration forms part of the natural life cycle of many species. Saussey (1966) found that in *Aporrectodea icterica* (p. 58) regeneration occurred only during the non-feeding stage of inactivity, diapause, induced by a drying out and rise in the temperatures of the soil. However, injury or the removal of the caudal region at any time caused the worms spontaneously to enter diapause regardless of the physical conditions. The mole, *Talpa europea*, exploits this behaviour to keep stores of fresh food. Plisko (1961) reported cephalic mutilation of worms in mole hills while Saussey (1966) described specimens of *Aporrectodea giardi*, *A. longa* and *Lumbricus terrestris* with their first three to five body segments bitten off lying curled up in diapause within the central chamber of a mole hill.

Cephalic regeneration is controlled by a neurosecretory hormone produced by the ganglia of the anterior segments, especially the cerebral ganglion. The number of segments, i.e. ganglia involved, varies specifically but there is always a gradient of decreasing secretory activity passing posteriorly. Hence it is only under laboratory conditions that an isolated posterior region can generate a new 'head' when a cerebral ganglion (or an extract) is implanted; while after anterior damage, a new 'head' will regenerate only when some neurosecretory ganglia survive. However, there is evidence that some control of caudal regeneration may, on the other hand, lie in the tissues adjacent to a cut surface (Moment, 1979). A wound in *Eisenia fetida* is at first sealed largely by a massive contraction of the circular muscles of the exposed, damaged segment. Next, scar tissue forms and with it begins the early stages of caudal regeneration leading to the development of a stump-like miniature tail region with numerous, fine replacement segments. In all cases the region gradually attains full size but the original number of segments is seldom regained. The periproct is not replicated entirely for the anus of an 'amputee' is usually circular whereas it is a slit in undamaged worms. Sometimes abnormal growth may occur during regeneration but aberrant individuals such as fork-tailed monsters, can also be produced during embryonic development.

Enemies and predators

The effect of predators on earthworm populations is difficult to assess and has never been attempted in Britain. Generally man constitutes the greatest threat to earthworm populations. Drainage schemes, deforestation (also afforestation especially by conifers), farming (by the action of both ploughing and the application of chemicals including insecticides) and urbanization destroy natural habitats with their resident populations. These areas are then colonized by a few common allochthonous species, i.e. generalized feeders mostly able to tolerate disturbance.

Earthworms are a major item of diet for the mole *Talpa europea* which is largely confined to soils with high earthworm populations where individual moles may eat 60 earthworms a day. Most earthworms are captured after entering a mole's subterranean tunnels; the mole either bites off the periproct before squeezing all earth in the intestine from the tail end or, if not eaten immediately, bites off the anterior 3–5 segments of the worms to induce diapause thus preventing escape from special storage chambers (*see above*, Regeneration). Earthworms are often seasonally the staple diet of other mammals such as badgers, hedgehogs, shrews, woodmice and otters. Foxes have been observed to catch 2–10 large, foraging *Lumbricus terrestris* on wet nights and owls too prey on this species at night when the worms emerge from their burrows. Many diurnal birds are able to detect worms within the soil, probably by hearing the faint sounds of scratching setae and squelching as the worms move through their burrows. Blackbirds, thrushes and robins are prominent predators in gardens and park land while flocks of starlings, rooks, lapwings and gulls can be important mortality factors in open grassland and in cultivation when following a plough or harrow (Cuendet, 1979). The herring gull by 'marking-time' or 'paddling' with its feet can stimulate earthworms in grassland to emerge from the soil as does the lapwing (Darwin, 1881:28). Macdonald (1983) gives fuller details of the predation on earthworms by terrestrial vertebrates.

Ants and the larvae and adults of several ground beetles, such as *Feronia madida* (Carabidae), and rove beetles (Staphylinidae), are predators but the effect of these insects on earthworm populations is unknown. Another invertebrate predator is the large, soil-dwelling jawless leech, *Trocheta subviridis*. This widespread yet rare species ingests an earthworm by coiling its body around the victim and swallowing the worm head first like a boa-constrictor crushing and consuming its prey.

Parasites

Records of the parasites of earthworms are imperfect (Stephenson, 1930:648). For the most part it seems that *Lumbricus terrestris* possesses more parasites than any other earthworm while there is a greater prevalence of infestation in German populations than elsewhere. The reasons for this situation is that in Europe, *Lumbricus terrestris* is more likely to be dissected than any other species and earthworms are commonly misidentified; while Germany has produced more parasitologists ready to study the parasites of earthworms than have other countries. Sporozoans especially of the genus *Monocystis*, are the commonest parasites of earthworms, usually infesting the seminal vesicles. Most have seemingly achieved an equilibrium with their host species since pathological conditions are rare. Recent additions to British records of gregarine sporozoans were listed by Segun (1971). Earthworms have also been reported to be the adventitious, intermediate or primary hosts of other parasites: Ciliata (protozoans); Trematoda (lungworms); Cestoda (tapeworms); Nematoda (roundworms) in addition to scattered reports of bacteria (for details *see*, Gates, 1972*a*, especially p. 122). Many of the parasites also occur in pigs, sheep, cattle, horses, dogs, cats and poultry.

Earthworms are seldom free from parasites especially *Monocystis* and the adventitious hosts of soil dwelling protozoans and nematodes, whether or not the latter micro-organisms are permanently free-living or have only transitory free-living stages in complex life cycles. Thus both plant (i.e. soil) nematodes and the larvae of poultry tapeworms have been found in the coeloms of eathworms in areas where these nematodes are common. (A phenomenon that can confuse the parasitologist when attempting to recognize the obligatory parasites of earthworms.) The effects that parasites have on earthworms are variable. Extreme conditions produced by lethal infestations are seldom observed since heavily parasitized worms will die and decay within their burrows. At the other extreme, nematode larvae may be discovered living freely in the coelomic fluid, for example hookworm larvae in tropical species, especially in the anterior segments of seemingly healthy, active earthworms. Between these extremes may be seen nodular cysts formed by Protozoa that may have little effect on the host or be so located as to obstruct ducts or pores (Sims, 1982*a* : 290). There is too the condition leading sometimes to parasitic castration caused by massive infestations of gregarine sporozoans in the seminal vesicles spreading to destroy the testes and through the vasa deferentia to the male pores causing the male ducts to atrophy. The effect at first may be to disrupt the flow of sperm to the exterior, then to reduce the maturation of sperm and finally to stop the production of spermatogonia. At the same time, the production of sex hormones will be affected and secondary sexual characters such as the tubercula pubertatis may fail to develop or to be only imperfectly formed, e.g. the '*trapezoides*' morph of *Aporrectodea caliginosa* (p. 54).

The effects of parasitization have been interpreted as evidence of parthenogenesis especially among introduced species that often have a high incidence of a pathological degradation of the male system. Introduced species have little tolerance of parasites new to them whereas the native species have evolved an equilibrium with the local parasites and survive with only mild infestations. Meanwhile the colonizing populations are maintained by the minority of their members that escape the depredation of the parasites. (*Note.* Some earthworms regularly reproduce parthenogenetically (Perel, 1982) while in other species parthenogenesis or self-fertilization may be induced by the isolation of individuals; Hartenstein, Neuhauser and Easton, 1980).

When the opportunity arises some insects may lay their eggs in earthworms. For example, the single larva of a cluster fly *Pollenia rudis* (Calliphoridae) has been found in *Allolobophora chlorotica* (p. 50) and in *Aporrectodea rosea* (p. 65). However, the species has not been recorded frequently in earthworms despite the abundance of the adult flies in the autumn.

Not all protozoans are harmful parasites. Some are commensals and may achieve a symbiotic relationship with their hosts. When *Eisenia fetida* (p. 80) was cultured in sterile soil to which soil fungi and bacteria were added, individuals failed to complete growth but on the addition of soil protozoa, worms grew to full size and achieved sexual maturity (Miles, 1963).

Ecology

Earthworms have evolved from aquatic, stenohaline freshwater ancestors to become adapted to life in moist terrestrial habitats but they cannot survive in dry soils. Several terrestrial species are still capable of living in the beds of lakes and rivers while others can survive long periods of submergence when the soil is flooded with freshwater but a few, non-lumbricoid species, are euryhaline and can survive inundation by seawater. Variations in the morphologies of the nephridial vesicles that govern osmo-regulation, have enabled the different species to adapt to various habitats covering a range of humidities. But behavioural changes are also important and these can contribute towards survival in dry seasons. During prolonged spells of dry weather, earthworms such as species of *Allolobophora* (p. 50), *Aporrectodea* (p. 53) and *Octolasion* (p. 112), retreat deeper into their burrow systems as the surface layers of the soil become increasingly arid. Here they coil-up into a tight knot within a small spherical chamber constructed by each worm and lined with its own moist faeces. Within the chambers the worms undergo a resting phase or period of quiescence and remain there until the rain falls and conditions become more favourable which cause the worms to become active again (Fig. 11). The permanent vertical burrows of *Lumbricus terrestris* (p. 106) in Britain may measure up to 3 m deep while the burrows of some tropical earthworms, e.g. family Megascolecidae, may extend even further down perhaps as deep as 15 m in areas where there are prolonged dry seasons. This transitory period of quiescence is controlled by external factors, low soil humidities or high soil temperatures, and is a form of aestivation. It is distinct from the period of obligatory inactivity, often triggered by physical conditions, brought about by other factors such as regeneration and known as diapause that was well documented by Saussey (1966) in *Aporrectodea icterica*.

Earthworms survive dry spells by becoming quiescent deep within the soil although they apparently slowly lose water since the terminal chambers of their burrows remain moist long after the surrounding soil has dried out. Meanwhile, newly hatched juveniles too feeble to burrow deeply and individuals that construct shallow chambers, may become desiccated and die.

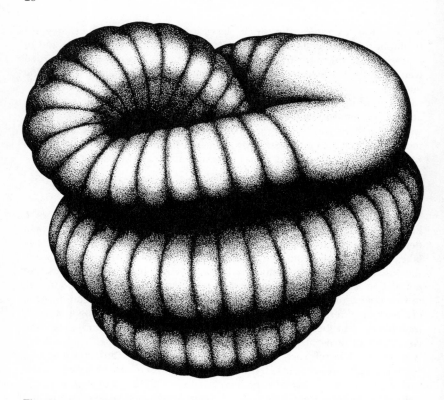

Fig. 11. An earthworm coiled during a resting period of quiescence or diapause. (© *British Museum* (*Natural History*), 1975.)

Surface browsing species of *Lumbricus* are confronted with additional water problems; the surface vegetation dries out during a long period of drought so little water is contained in the diet, then while foraging on the surface, water is lost by evaporation from the coelomic fluid secreted to keep the body moist for respiration. *Lumbricus terrestris* (p. 106) eventually retreats to a terminal chamber of the burrow usually about 60–120 cm deep, where it coils around a bed of pea-sized stones to conserve moisture. Unless diapause is obligatory, most pasture dwelling worms are fully active throughout the summer in Britain where the soils remain irrigated and are kept permanently moist near a field capacity of pF 2.0 (Gerard, 1967).

In Britain cold moist periods affect feeding and copulation less than warm dry periods. During cold spells worms also retreat deep into the soil where they undergo an enforced quiescence. Being poikilothermic animals, the levels of their activities are governed largely by temperature, so these transitory periods of winter quiescence are dissimilar to the true hibernation of some higher animals. Embryonic development continues but at a decreasing rate as the temperate falls or the pF is reduced and hatching is delayed until thresholds are exceeded.

Earthworms are often expelled from their burrows when the ground becomes water-logged after heavy rain. The species *Octolasion cyaneum* (p. 112) was observed to leave the soil on one occasion when the rainfall exceeded 6.0 mm while *Aporrectodea rosea* (p. 65) is almost as sensitive. Flooding causes the burrows to become filled with de-oxygenated, acidic ground water; this has mainly a deleterious physiological effect on the immersed earthworms judging by the flaccid condition of many individuals expelled from their burrows and found wandering across paths after rain.

Water and temperature are the most important factors in the ecology of earthworms and each is a major influence in seasonal activity, perhaps being key factors for mortality. But there are other, perhaps equally important, factors governing the distribution and size of earthworm populations: soil type and acidity (pH), the humus, i.e. the nitrogen content, structure of the population of micro-organisms, the vegetable cover and not least, the level of disturbance by man (Satchell, 1955). The availability of food regularly limits population sizes but the significance of this single factor is not constant in all habitats (Lakhani and Satchell, 1970). Generally species with narrow environmental requirements have localized distributions while those with a wide tolerance are among the commonest in occurrence (Cuendet, 1984).

Distinct ecological groups can be recognized among the Lumbricidae. Bouché (1971, 1972, 1976) separated the French earthworms into three categories mainly on the following morphological and behavioural (physiological) characters.

A. *Litter dwellers—mesophagous, epigeic species.*

1. Colouration usually red, vinaceous or rosy (adaptation to litter).
2. Anterior septa, musculature reduced (no burrowing).
3. Body wall, longitudinal muscles, structure generally pennate.
4. High mobility (adaptation to evade predators).
5. Respiratory rate relatively high.
6. Regeneration, ability reduced.
7. Nephridiopores do *not* form a regular line along the body.
8. Diapause unknown only ecologically induced quiescence caused by low humidity or temperature.
9. Caudal region cylindrical.
10. Small size.

Under normal conditions these earthworms live outside of the mineral substrata, occurring in litter, decomposing tree-trunks, compost etc. Deforestation usually causes local extinction. The characters have arisen by the selective effective of predators and in response to life in changeable temporary microhabitats. Heavily pigmented species such as *Lumbricus castaneus* (p. 96), *L. rubellus* (p. 104), *Dendrobaena octaedra* (p. 70), *Dendrodrilus rubidus* (p. 76) and *Satchellius mammalis* (p. 118) are typical members of the group.

B. *Deep burrowers—macrophagous, anecic species.*

1. Colouration normally brown to brown black, perhaps iridescent (protective colouration).
2. Anterior septa, musculature well developed and funnel-shaped, highly active burrower, surface browser and food withdrawn into burrow.
3. Body wall, longitudinal muscles, structure radial sometimes pennate.
4. Highly contractile, capable of rapid retreat through burrows.
5. Regeneration well-developed.
6. Nephridiopres do *not* form a regular line along the body, i.e. increased effectiveness for moistening the epidermis.
7. Diapause common, often obligatory.
8. Caudal region depressed, paddle-shaped.
9. Size moderate to large.

This group comprises the soil-dwelling earthworms with vertical burrows. They commonly emerge at night to feed on the surface litter, lying with the caudal region secured within the mouth of the burrow. They often survive deforestation and some can withstand cultivation. They are characterized by their intense burrowing abilities and the production of burrow complexes; some cast onto the surface of the soil. Despite some characters shared with the horizontal burrowing species, this group has greater affinity with the litter dwellers and like them has evolved special characters in response to predation. Members of this group include the larger species of the genus *Aporrectodea* (p. 53) and, outside of Great Britain, *Scherotheca* and *Eophila*.

C. *Horizontal burrowers—microphagous, endogeic species.*

1. Cutaneous pigmentation absent.
2. Anterior septa, musculature well developed; funnel-shaped (root-feeders, 'rhizophagous') or not (soil-feeders, 'geophagous').
3. Body wall, longitudinal musculature, structure variable.
4. Body diameter, moderate to slight or very slender.
5. Regeneration, ability variable (largely unknown).
6. Nephridiopores usually form a regular line.
7. Diapause (?)
8. Caudal region cylindrical.
9. Size small to moderate.

The members of this group are truly animals of the soil, they live permanently in essentially horizontal burrows in the mineralo-organic substratum of the soil. Here their food consists of dead roots and both microflora and -fauna ingested with the soil (geophagy). They cast below the surface of the soil. This category is less homogenous than the other two, especially in the food preferences of its members. Most of the (group) characters indicate adaptation to living continuously within the soil, e.g. the lack of pigmentation in the body wall. Species of the genus *Octolasion* (p. 112) are typical members of this group.

The characters of the three biological groups recognized among the European Lumbricidae, illustrate clearly the degree of morphological change that has occurred in response to ecology; although undoubtedly there are also parallel physiological adaptations. These categories provide useful concepts in the study of earthworms although not all species can be readily assigned to a single group. *Aporrectodea caliginosa* (p. 54) is essentially a horizontal burrower yet it has brown pigment while its *nocturna* morph, the fully developed phenotype, can be identified as a deep burrower; then although *Lumbricus terrestris* is a deep burrowing species it can be considered to be a litter dweller due to its range of habitats and red pigmentation (Bouché, 1972, Table 16).

The three ecological types recognized by Bouché developed from the earlier concept of dividing the Lumbricidae into two ecological groups: surface-living red-pigmented forms and soil-dwelling non-red-pigmented forms. These categories were reviewed by Satchell (1980) who went on to suggest that the contrasting behaviour, morphology and physiology of the two forms represent evolutionary poles arising from r and K selection. This is an important contribution and provides an excellent introduction to earthworm ecology, the bibliography is particularly useful (*see also* Satchell, 1958; Wallwork, 1983).

Obviously the morphological and behavioural categories recognized among European Lumbricidae are not directly applicable to all members of other families elsewhere (for example, the arboreal *Planapheretima*, family Megascolecidae, of Asia). In addition there are undoubtedly further categories to be recognized among members of aquatic and semi-aquatic families, the boreal Biwadrilidae, Lutodrilidae and Sparganonphilidae also the tropical Almidae and many members of the Ocnerodrilidae. Clearly recognition of the characters appropriate to each ecological type also helps to distinguish whether characters are adaptive and so apomorphic (recent) or pleisiomorphic (primitive) (Bouché, 1980, 1983).

World distributions

The present day distributions of the majority of the true earthworms forming the suborder Lumbricina, seemingly reflect past palaeogeographic events (Sims, 1980; Bouché, 1983). Apart from the monotypic superfamilies Criodriloidea from southeastern Europe, Asia Minor and the Levant and the Biwadriloidea from Japan, the other three component superfamilies have ranges that for the most part can be correlated with past changes in continental boundaries. The superfamily Lumbricoidea is broadly confined to parts of the ancient northern landmass of Laurasia forming the old Mesozoic continent of Euramerica which existed in late Cretaceous times some 65 million years ago prior to the opening of the north Atlantic. This land mass extended in the west from the Mid-Continental Seaway which separated eastern from western North America eastwards to the Turgai Straits between the European and Asian plates joining the northern polar sea with the Tethys Sea. Confirmation of long residence by the family Lumbricidae in eastern North America was provided by Schwert (1979) when he reported the discovery of a fossil capsule of *Dendrodrilus rubidus* in sediments some 10 000 years in age from Ontario. Although a few indigenous lumbricoid species are now found in eastern Asia (Perel, 1979), none occurs (naturally) in western North America except for a few species of the family Sparganophilidae. The natural distribution of the aquatic family Sparganophilidae is not clear but dispersal facilitated by reversals, captures and other changes in river systems, may account for the presence of indigenous species in the western United States away from the southeastern states, the seeming homeland of the family (Reynolds, 1980). The number of lumbricoid species is greatest in the southern region of the old continent, Euramerica, which escaped the rigours of the Pleistocene glaciations. Nearly 400 species of the family Lumbricidae are recognized, mostly from the south, with only about 5% now inhabiting the northern areas once overlain by the ice sheets. The comparative richness of the fauna in the areas to the south is reflected in the distributions of other lumbricoid families and also the monotypic superfamily Criodriloidea which is confined to a small part of this southern area. The family Hormogastridae occurs in countries of the western Mediterranean, the family Ailoscolecidae in the central Pyrenees, North Carolina, Tennessee and Indiana while the family Lutodrilidae is confined to southeastern Louisiana. The effects of some of the greatest events in the long history of the old southern continent of Gondwana, the separation of Africa from South America with the opening of the south Atlantic and the detachment of both peninsular India and Madagascar from eastern Africa can be seen in the distribution of members of the superfamily Glossoscolecidae. These events together with the isolation of Australia and the separation of many Pacific fragments are reflected in the wide ranging distributions of the largest superfamily, Megascolecoidea.

Origins of the British earthworm fauna

The Lumbricidae is the only widespread family of earthworms occurring throughout the vast area once forming the Mesozoic continent of Euramerica. It contains some 385 valid species (Easton, 1983), most of which are endemic to those small areas of southern Europe which escaped the ice sheets and permafrost during the Pleistocene and Quaternary glaciations, i.e. within the Franco-Iberian region west of the Alps and to the east, the Balkan and Transcaucasian regions. In contrast, about 20 species are now distributed throughout much of the Palaearctic and temperate regions of the Nearctic in addition to the Neotropical and Australasian regions, South Africa and many oceanic islands, especially those of the southern oceans, i.e. wherever European crops have been introduced or ships' ballast of soil discharged. These widespread species were formerly termed peregrine ('wandering'), sometimes anthropochorous ('transported by man'), but more recently allochthonous ('exogenous', originating outside of a given area). (The opposite term autochthonous is employed for 'endogenous' i.e. indigenous species.) The recent terms are preferred for allochthonous can also be applied to euryhaline species of tropical families passively transported on drifting vegetation. Most allochothonous species have wide habitat tolerances and are geophagous feeders living in temporary burrows so they can survive disturbance and often benefit from cultivation due to an enhanced food supply. Many are commonly intercepted during quarantine inspections carried out on soil containing imported plants. Several of these species are parthenogenetic so even a single individual if introduced into a new area, can reproduce and possibly cause the species to spread. Once established, they usually colonize urban and cultivated areas where native earthworms have become scarce or locally extinct. The widespread allochthonous species predominate in cultivated soils in areas of northern Europe and Asia that were affected by the glaciations during the Pleistocene. The distribution suggests that in these areas the original earthworm faunas were exterminated during the glacial epochs and were subsequently colonized northwards, after the retreat of the ice, by species capable of active or passive distribution (Gates, 1970).

The Ice Age must have had a marked effect on the British fauna. The ice sheets advanced and retreated several times; during the maximum of the Pleistocene glacial advances (in the Weichselian glaciation, about 15 000 BP), the whole of Scotland, Ireland, Wales and most of England were covered with permafrost and possibly at least temporarily, with ice. The Lumbricidae were exterminated from the British Isles and the species found today have come from continental Europe.

Recolonization could have started across the land-bridge created from the post-glacial deposits that connected Belgium and Norfolk between 13 000 and 8 300 BP until the North Sea was formed after a world-wide rise in sea level. Like members of the exotic families, some species have undoubtedly been introduced by man, for example *Aporrectodea icterica* (p. 58) and *Eisenia hortensis* (p. 84) which usually occur in cultivation or near gardens containing imported plants. Probably other species too have been adventitiously introduced. Most British earthworms are recognized as allochthonous species, of the remaining half-a-dozen we can only speculate about how they came to inhabit these islands and whether more remain to be discovered.

Earthworms and Man

Earthworms are central to the survival of man because of the importance of their activities in the production of our food. They play a major ecological role by breaking down plant and humic matter to release nitrogen compounds for assimilation by plants. Also they increase the water retaining capacity of the soil by changing its physical character with the crumb structure of their faeces, the result of the action of bacteria and fungi during the passage of food and soil through the alimentary canal. Soil drainage and aeration also are improved by the burrows of earthworms that additionally provide channels for the easy penetration of plant roots (Graff and Makeschin, 1979). Agricultural studies have shown both the beneficial actions of earthworms in crop production and the agricultural practices that pose threats to earthworms: ploughing, applications of insecticides, herbicides etc. also stubble burning that affects some species (Davey, 1963; Gerard and Hay, 1979; Edwards, 1983). There is now a growing awareness of the need for improvements in agricultural techniques to encourage maximum earthworm populations (Edwards, 1980). Extensive field tests have revealed the agricultural preparations and rates of application that directly increase the mortality rate of earthworms (Edwards, 1979) and the agriculture techniques that affect earthworm population structures. When the traditional agricultural custom of ploughing is replaced by modern methods of cultivation employing herbicidal sprays to destroy the residues of previous crops, weeds etc., geophagous earthworms inhabiting temporary burrows, such as *Aporrectodea caliginosa* (p. 54), become scarcer while surface browsing species inhabiting permanent burrows, for example *Lumbricus terrestris* (p. 106), become more numerous. Here the shift in the structure of the earthworm populations is caused by a reduction in the available food for the geophagous species whereas the absence of disturbance through the cessation of ploughing, favours the permanent burrow dwellers (Edwards and Lofty, 1975). Most insecticides do not kill earthworms when used at the rates recommended by the manufacturers. However, many may not be broken down by the worm's metabolism nor excreted so they may accumulate as sub-lethal residues that reduce breeding rates or kill in the long term. Similarly birds (or their eggs) and other predatory animals that regularly feed on contaminated earthworms can be affected by accumulations of these poisons.

In Britain, legislation against the pollution of the enviroment or the common law of causing a nuisance by the emission of offensive odours, cause problems for the modern factory farms that need to dispose of large accumulations of faeces from intensive livestock units housing poultry, rabbits, pigs or cattle (Cotton and Curry, 1980*a* and *b*). Increasingly advantage is now being taken of the activities of those species of earthworms, such as *Eisenia fetida* (p. 80), that can process most decaying plant and animal waste while it remains aerobic. Worms convert the waste into friable, odourless materials that can then be disposed of without further treatment and spread over fields as a fertilizer (Appelhof, 1980 and 1981; Kretschmar, 1983). Not only may these various procedures provide a practical and economical solution for the disposal of organic residues but the earthworms themselves can be marketed as high protein food for livestock, poultry, fish and pets. Pigs reared under experimental conditions have an increased growth rate when given a protein supplement to their diet of *Eisenia fetida* cultured in pig manure. This earthworm is the species most commonly used as an animal food in temperate regions although it can be cultured in the tropics; in Kenya, for example, it is bred in vegetable mulch on fish farms as a food for *Tilapia*. Generally local species are preferred and in the Far East, *Perionyx excavatus* (p. 134) is commonly cultured. In the Philippines this species has been bred in vegetable waste then processed with herbs and seasoning to make steaklets for human consumption. Although this preparation scored high in palatability tests, there was a rapid consumer disenchantment when the identity of the protein content was divulged (Guerro, 1983 and personal communication). The general principles of the methods for culturing large populations of earthworms can be gleaned from a wide range of publications, e.g. Barrett, 1949; Minnich, 1977; Edwards and Lofty, 1977; Reinecke and Kriel, 1981. Generally, the ecological strategies developed during the course of earthworm evolution, suggest the roles that the different species can play in vermiculture (Satchell, 1981).

Earthworms have always played a part in the affairs of man (Stephenson, 1930:657). In rural districts of Japan, earthworms are used in the 'Niimi process' for purifying household waste water (Nakamura, 1982). While many primitive peoples have commonly used them for food as do some remote tribes of South America at the present day, especially the giant species of the family Glossoscolecidae, by removing the soil from the gut and cooking them with vegetables. Generally throughout history earthworms have been used in medicine in the belief that they have curative properties for a range of human ailments and conditions, from a hair restorer to an aphrodisiac and even as a treatment for haemorrhoids. Although there is no evidence to support these beliefs, current research shows that man may yet find unsuspected uses for earthworms (Sabine, 1983).

Practical methods

Collection

Earthworms may need to be collected for several reasons: for a faunal survey of an ecotype or an area, a study of the soil biomass, the composition and dynamics of soil populations, to obtain specimens for class instruction, bait for angling or food for laboratory animals. As each species has strong ecological preferences, collecting sites need to be selected carefully. To obtain specimens of the small *Dendrobaena* (p. 68) species, it is necessary to sort forest litter and search under moss and the bark of fallen trees (or collect litter samples and recover the earthworms in the laboratory by heat extraction techniques using a Berlese-type funnel). Whereas the large *Lumbricus* (p. 96) and *Aporrectodea* (p. 53) species can be collected from soil in meadows and parkland by chemical extraction or digging. Species of exotic families however are more likely to occur in well-cultivated gardens especially those with greenhouses containing imported plants.

Earthworms may be picked up when driven from their burrows by ground water following heavy rain. Anglers may stimulate earthworms to leave their burrows by vibrating a metal bar or garden fork dug into the soil, even by tapping the sole of their foot on the soil for a few minutes. Then when the temperature and humidity are suitable, species such as *Lumbricus terrestris* emerge at night either leaving the burrow or lying with the caudal region within the burrow entrance. On these occasions worms can be picked up under torchlight but stealth is essential as they are sensitive to vibration and light, withdrawing rapidly at the approach of the collector. Generally, however, other collecting techniques are employed (Edwards and Lofty, 1977).

Techniques

The methods selected for collecting earthworms are determined by sampling requirements. Comparative sampling methods are used when statistical analysis requires a number of replicate samples to be collected over a period in a uniform habitat, for example, monitoring populations in plots that have received chemical dressings. One technique employed is to bait traps of wide meshed bags with dung, compost or soil from the test plot, then bury them for a discrete period before recovery and examination of the acquired fauna. Alternatively, entomological pit-fall traps (containers buried in the soil with their mouths level with the surface) can be used to sample individuals that roam at night from their burrows.

It is more common, however, for other sampling techniques to be used. The most popular methods are: hand-sorting, chemical and electrical extraction; a combination of hand-sorting and chemical extraction techniques being the most effective for bio-assays (Terhivuo, 1982).

Hand-sorting. Soil is dug using a quick levering action to intercept rapidly retreating large worms, then spread on a plastic sheet for handsorting or sealed in plastic bags for transport to a laboratory for later examination. For quantitative studies, a known volume of soil is removed for each sample. In addition to simple hand-sorting, these samples can also be treated with chemicals, washed through sieves or separated by flotation methods to ensure the recovery of the smallest juveniles and capsules (Macfadyen, 1963 and 1975; Southwood, 1979) when absolute estimates of earthworm populations are required.

Chemical extraction. Irritants are employed to expel earthworms from the soil when they can be picked up with forceps (irritants stimulate worms to secrete mucus copiously making them difficult to handle). Suitable irritants are solutions of mustard and water, commercial vermifuges, potassium permanganate and formalin. The last, formalin solution, is commonly used as it is the most effective and is not lethal to earthworms if the solution is prepared correctly, neither killing worms in the soil nor harming them if they are washed briefly in clean fresh water when they emerge from their burrows. Moreover it does not damage clothing worn by the collector nor stain his hands. However care must be excercised when handling *concentrated* commercial formalin and a safety mask and gloves should be worn. A suitable solution is prepared by adding 25 ml of concentrated commercial formalin (approximately 40% formaldehyde solution) to five litres of water (one quarter cupful to one gallon). This is applied to half a square metre of soil using a garden watering can with a sprinkler rose. The application is repeated when the worms stop emerging from the soil. The volume and dilution of the solution may be varied according to the soil type and water content. Care must always be exercised to avoid strong solutions otherwise the worms may be killed in the soil. If formalin is not available, a suitable solution of potassium permanganate can be used as a substitute by dissolving 10 g of crystals in five litres of water (one half ounce in one gallon) but this will not only expel the worms from the soil but also poison them as well.

Electrical methods. Less effective than either of the foregoing, these techniques are suitable for sampling experimental plots and other sites where chemicals may not be applied nor the soil dug. An alternating current of 2–4 amps from a mains supply (positive) is made to discharge from an electrode plunged into the soil and pass to the 'mains' earth. Electrical methods must always be operated with great caution. The effectiveness of this technique is dependent on the conductivity of the soil which is largely governed by the soil water content; generally it is inferior to other methods.

Preservation

Earthworms collected for population counts or biomass records can be placed directly into a 4% formaldehyde solution (i.e. 10% solution of concentrated commercial formalin). If the preserved worms are kept at a low temperature and placed on blotting paper until the upper body surface becomes dry before weighing, their mass will not alter for seven days (Gerard and Hay, 1979). Prolonged storage in dilute formalin causes specimens to become brittle and unsuitable for dissection. Earthworms for reference collections and morphological studies should be relaxed before killing. Several anaesthetic solutions are effective with 5–10% ethyl alcohol (perfumery grade) among the most convenient although 12–25% solutions of vodka, gin or white rum can be used. After 1–15 minutes in the anaesthetic solution the specimens become limp and when they no longer respond to gentle prodding, can be straightened out on damp tissue or filter paper in a flat dish and killed by the addition of a small quantity of a fixative solution. Material for taxonomic or anatomical studies can be fixed in 4% solution of formaldehyde (i.e. 10% solution of concentrated formalin) or histological fixatives such as Bouin's or Zenker's fluids. After 24 hours in the fixative the worms can be washed and stored in 80% ethyl alcohol or for storage of only a few months in a 1% solution of propylene phenoxetol. Ideally the specimens should not fill more than half of the container which should be completely filled with preservative before sealing (evaporation will damage specimens if they dry out). The preservative should be renewed after the first month since it will become diluted by the water in the bodies of the worms.

Data recording

It is best to label material in the field at the time of collection otherwise a reference number to a field notebook entry should be written on a label. Minimal data recorded should include at least: the date, location (grid number) and brief ecological notes, e.g. soil type, and its water content, habitat, etc. Labels should always be placed inside the container, never gummed or tied outside. Labels for immersion in a preservative should be of good quality paper, ideally they should be made of goat-skin parchment. Waterproof indian ink is suitable for writing labels but the ink must be allowed to dry thoroughly before immersion. Labels may also be written with a soft lead pencil but ball point pens should *never* be used.

When collections are being made in association with ecological surveys, it may be convenient to record data on specially prepared field record cards. Cards of this sort have been designed and prepared by the Biological Records Centre, Monks Wood Experimental Station, Abbots Ripton, Huntingdon, PE17 2LS, Great Britain, an organization responsible for collecting data on the distribution of much of the British flora and fauna. Data from the cards are eventually stored on magnetic tape or disc, and can be selectively retrieved in cartographic or tabular form to meet the needs of ecologists and organizations concerned with conservation. (For additional information on collection, preservation, storage etc., *see* Lincoln and Sheals, 1979).

Examination

The adults of British earthworms can usually be distinguished on external characters and experienced collectors need only a good hand-lens to identify most living worms in the field. However, preserved material is best examined in the laboratory under a low-power binocular microscope. Beginners should attempt at first to identify only clitellate specimens since problems are encountered when examining aclitellate (juvenile or immature) specimens and these can be overcome only with experience. A specimen for study is best examined under water in a dissection dish or tray with paraffin wax over the bottom. Usually only a small pair of watchmakers' forceps will be required for manipulation during examination and possibly fine entomological pins for fastening specimens to the wax. Otherwise if dissection becomes necessary a pair of needles in handles, a fine seeker and a pair of small, sharp-pointed scissors (entomological or ophthalmic) will be needed. Before beginning an examination it is sometimes necessary to remove the cuticle if it has become detached from the epidermis and obscures fine details

Table 1

External characters for the rapid identification of adult British Lumbricidae

DORSAL SURFACE	
Primary character	Prostomium: epilobic/tanylobic
Confirmatory characters	Size mm
	Pigmentation: colour
	pattern
	First dorsal pore: location
	Number of segments
VENTRAL SURFACE	
Primary characters	Post-clitellar setal distances:
	closely paired/widely paired/distant
	Males pores: size
	inconspicuous
	with large tumescences
	confined to a single segment
	larger
	Tubercula pubertatis: location
	number
	shape
Confirmatory characters	Clitellum: size
	location
	Post-clitellar setal formula:
	Setae with genital tumescences: location

of structure. This is easily done by using the scissors to make an incision in the cuticle about midway along the body, then with the seeker raising the cuticle, cut laterally around the body to produce two halves that can be stripped off.

It is convenient to begin studying a specimen by examining the dorsal surface which is frequently more heavily pigmented than the ventral surface. Next the specimen can be rolled onto its side to establish the relative positions of the lateral setae (possibly also the nephridipores and any other pores). Finally the ventral surface should be examined when perhaps due to curling, it may be convenient to straighten and secure specimens by pinning the anterior and posterior extremities of the body to the wax. The principal external characters to be examined for the identification of mature British lumbricids are listed in Table 1. Internal structures need to be examined to observe generic characters or for the identification of some introduced species. Dissection is carried out by pinning the worm ventral surface downwards taking care that the pin holding the anterior end passes behind the prostomium but through the pharynx. A longitudinal median dorsal incision is made with the scissors, cutting forwards carefully through only the body wall from about segment *xxv* to the pharynx (in practice the incision should be slightly to one side of the mid-dorsal line so that when present, the dorsal pores remain intact). Care should be exercised to avoid damaging internal structures particularly the intestine when soil will be liberated making inspection difficult and irrigation with water from a pipette necessary.

Systematics

The current classification of the class Oligochaeta recognizes three constituent orders: Lumbriculida (freshwater worms with affinities with the commensal, leech-like Branchiobdellida), Moniligastrida (soil-dwelling, earthworm group of India, southeast Asia, southern and central China) and the Haplotaxida (all other Oligochaeta* including the true earthworms). The earthworms are placed in the suborder Lumbricina which is characterized by the clitellum being formed from multiple layers of cells and the oöcytes being microlecithal, i.e. small with little yolk. (All other Oligochaeta have the clitellum composed of a single layer of cells and have macrolecithal oöcytes, i.e. large, yolky eggs.) The classification of the Lumbricina has been the subject of controversy but the system adopted here is now gaining acceptance (Sims, 1980 and 1982*b*). Twenty-four families and subfamilies are recognized from all parts of the world except Antarctica. They are grouped into superfamilies on the structure of the ovary and the manner of shedding the oöcytes, i.e. whether budded individually or grouped in single or multiple egg-strands; two monotypic and three polytypic superfamilies are recognized.

The mutual affinities of the five families forming the Lumbricina are unknown and in the absence of a fossil record likely to remain problematic. The two monotypic superfamilies, Criodriloidea and Biwadriloidea, are aquatic and being morphologically less specialized than other earthworms, can be regarded as more primitive. Their present distributions are restricted and may well be relicts of wider, older ranges perhaps dating to late Palaeozoic times and the ancient supercontinent of Pangaea. Their affinities are obscure but the southern Palaearctic Criodriloidea has seemingly greater affinity with the Holarctic Lumbricoidea while the Japanese Biwadriloidea possesses slight similarity with the predominantly southern superfamilies Glossoscolecoidea and Megascolecoidea. (Earlier discussions of affinities often attached great significance to adaptive and negative (absent) characters causing these two monotypic superfamilies to be associated with other aquatic families.) The affinities of the southern superfamilies are slender but are possibly mutually greater than with the northern Lumbricoidea.

---

*The families Aelosomatidae and Branchiobdellidae are separated as monotypic classes co-ordinate with the Oligochaeta and the Hirudinea in the subphylum Clitellata. There are, however, dissenting views (Brinkhurst, 1982).

Classification**

Phylum ANNELIDA
Subphylum CLITELLATA
Class OLIGOCHAETA
Order HAPLOTAXIDA
Suborder LUMBRICINA
Superfamily CRIODRILOIDEA*
Superfamily LUMBRICOIDEA
Family SPARGANOPHILIDAE Michaelsen, 1928
  Sparganophilus tamesis Benham, 1892
Family AILOSCOLECIDAE Bouché, 1969 (inc. Komarekionidae, Gates, 1974*a*)*
Family HORMOGASTRIDAE Michaelsen, 1900*
Family LUMBRICIDAE Rafinesque-Schmaltz, 1815
  Subfamily LUMBRICINAE Rafinesque-Schmaltz, 1815
    Allolobophora chlorotica (Savigny, 1826)
    Aporrectodea caliginosa (Savigny, 1826)
      inc. *nocturna* (Evans, 1946)
        trapezoides (Dugès, 1828)
        tuberculata (Eisen, 1874)
    Aporrectodea icterica (Savigny, 1826)
    Aporrectodea limicola (Michaelsen, 1890)
    Aporrectodea longa (Ude, 1885)
    Aporrectodea rosea (Savigny, 1826)
    Dendrobaena attemsi (Michaelsen, 1902)
    Dendrobaena octaedra (Savigny, 1826)
    Dendrobaena pygmaea (Savigny, 1826)
    Dendrodrilus rubidus (Savigny, 1826)
    Eisenia andrei Bouché, 1972
    Eisenia fetida (Savigny, 1826)
    Eisenia hortensis (Michaelsen, 1890)
    Eisenia veneta (Rosa, 1886)
    Eiseniella tetraedra (Savigny, 1826)
    Helodrilus oculatus Hoffmeister, 1845
    Lumbricus castaneus (Savigny, 1826)
    Lumbricus eiseni Levinsen, 1884
    Lumbricus festivus (Savigny, 1826)
    Lumbricus friendi Cognetti, 1904
    Lumbricus rubellus Hoffmeister, 1843
    Lumbricus terrestris Linnaeus, 1758
    Murchieona minuscula (Rosa, 1906)

**Superfamilies and families marked * have not been recorded in the British Isles, genera and species marked † were once reported but have not survived.

Octolasion cyaneum (Savigny, 1826)
Octolasion tyrtaeum tyrtaeum (Savigny, 1826)
Satchellius mammalis (Savigny, 1826)
    Subfamily DIPORODRILINAE Bouché, 1970*
    Family LUTODRILIDAE McMahan, 1976*
Superfamily BIWADRILOIDEA*
Superfamily GLOSSOSCOLECOIDEA
    Family KYNOTIDAE Jamieson, 1971*
    Family MICROCHAETIDAE Michaelsen, 1900*
    Family GLOSSOSCOLECIDAE Michaelsen, 1900
        Pontoscolex corethrurus (F. Müller, 1857)
    Family ALMIDAE Duboscq, 1902*
Superfamily MEGASCOLECOIDEA
    Family MEGASCOLECIDAE Rosa, 1891
        Amynthas corticis (Kinberg, 1867)
        Amynthas gracilis (Kinberg, 1867)
        Amynthas morrisi (Beddard, 1892a)[†]
        Amynthas rodericensis (Grube, 1879)[†]
        Metaphire californica (Kinberg, 1867)[†]
        Metaphire posthuma (Vaillant, 1868)[†]
        Metaphire schmardae (Horst, 1883)[†]
        Perionyx excavatus Perrier, 1872
        Spenceriella minor (Spencer, 1900)
    Family OCNERODRILIDAE Beddard, 1891[†]
        Eukerria Michaelsen, 1935[†]
        Gordiodrilus Beddard, 1892b[†]
        Nannodrilus Beddard, 1894[†]
        Nematogenia Eisen, 1900[†]
    Family ACANTHODRILIDAE Claus, 1880
        Microscolex phosphoreus (Dugès, 1837)
    Family OCTOCHAETIDAE Michaelsen, 1900
        Dichogaster bolaui (Michaelsen, 1891)
    Family EUDRILIDAE Claus, 1880
        Eudrilus eugeniae (Kinberg, 1867)

Taxonomy of British earthworms

The current list of British earthworms differs from the lists of species in earlier edition of the original synopsis *No 6 Lumbricidae* (Černosvitov and Evans, 1947; revised Gerard, 1964). Foremost are the inclusions of several introduced species of exotic families, two new records and the deletion of a species of Lumbricidae, also the changes caused by the revision of the Irish earthworms (Cotton, 1978). Equally noticeable are the changes due to advances in taxonomy (Zicsi, 1982; Sims, 1983), the most important being due to the adoption of the classification of the Lumbricidae proposed by

Gates (1975a, 1976a and 1982). This system is based primarily on the morphologies of the calciferous glands, the nephridial vesicles and, to a lesser extent, pigmentation; thus it is a synthesis of previous classifications proposed by Pop (1941), Omodeo (1956) and Perel (1976). It was originally applied to species occurring in North America but it is equally applicable to the lumbricids of northwestern Europe. However, at present, the more diverse earthworm fauna elsewhere in Europe has not been subjected to the same criteria so it has not been widely accepted (Zicsi, 1982; Easton, 1983).

The adoption of Gates's classification causes the rejection of the subfamilies previously recognized (Omodeo, 1956) and the introduction of new generic names. Gates described the genera *Satchellius* (1975a : 4) and *Murchieona* (1978a : 114) for species previously listed as *Dendrobaena mammalis* and *Bimastos muldali*. The last species was named by Omodeo (1956) for *Allolobophora minima* Muldal, 1952 (preoccupied by *minima* Rosa, 1884), an amphimictic worm not recognized as being conspecific with the parthenogenetic *icenorum* Pickford, 1926. All three specific names now disappear from the British list for after examination of the type specimens, Zicsi (1981) found the three to be synonymous with *minuscula* Rosa, 1906. The genus *Dendrodrilus*, up-graded from a subgenus of *Dendrobaena*, enters the British list to accommodate the species *rubidus* so removing this worm's association with *veneta* Rosa, 1886 and its allies which, incidentally, revert to the genus *Eisenia*. These last species formed a taxonomic tangle that has now been successfully unravelled. Michaelsen (1902) separated a heavily pigmented, striped form from the Caucasus as *zebra* that subsequently was found to occur throughout most of the range of *veneta*. It is now clear that the 'zebra-form' is a phenotype that occurs from time to time in most places according to fluctuations in local conditions and cannot be recognized taxonomically. Perhaps the most marked differences between the new list and its predecessors is the reduction in the size of the genus *Allolobophora*, now represented in Britain only by its type-species *chlorotica*. Other British species once included in this former catch-all genus, have been transferred to *Aporrectodea* Örley, 1885 (type-species *trapezoides* Dugès, 1828, a junior synonym of *caliginosa* Savigny, 1826). (A synonym of this genus is *Nicodrilus* Bouché (1972), type-species "*terrestris*: Savigny, 1826" = *giardi* Ribaucourt, 1901 (Bouché, 1976).) The commonest British species of *Aporrectodea* is *caliginosa* (Savigny, 1826). Zicsi (1982) was of the opinion that it is not only synonymous with both *trapezoides* Dugès, 1828 and *tuberculata* Eisen, 1874 but also with *nocturna* Evans, 1946 although some field workers disagree about sinking the last name (Bouché, 1972 : 337). Zicsi saw *caliginosa* as a single variable species with several developmental phases and phenotypes influenced by local conditions with the ecology and behaviour varying with size. The name *turgida* Eisen, 1873 is used by some North American authors for *caliginosa* Savigny, 1826 on the grounds that Savigny's species was originally inadequately defined whereas the identity of Eisen's species is beyond doubt. However, they overlook the subsequent restriction and usage by other authors, e.g. Michaelsen (1900), that validate the application of Savigny's name of the grey worm or turgid worm as it was once known to anglers. (The same fallacy has caused some authors to attempt to replace *Dendrobaena pygmaea* (Savigny, 1826) by *cognettii* (Michaelsen, 1903) although another, older name, *minima* Rosa, 1884, is available. Perhaps the solution lies in the designation of neotypes for the oldest names under the provisions of Article 75 of the *International Code of Zoological Nomenclature.*) Another species now included in the genus *Aporrectodea* is *icterica* (Savigny, 1826) after a fleeting inclusion in *Eophila.*

Two species of Lumbricidae have been added to the British list. The first, *Eisenia andrei* is an enigma. It is uniformly coloured but otherwise resembles the common striped species *Eisenia fetida.* (Note too the change in spelling from the incorrect, invalid emendation *foetida* to the original orthography of *fetida.*) The second addition occurred when Sims and Zicsi discovered *Dendrobaena attemsi* in Cumbria in September, 1981. The single species *Bimastos parvus* has now been removed from the list since there is no reliable evidence that the species has been recorded in the British Isles. With the removal of *parvus* and the transfer of *eiseni* (Levinsen, 1884) to the genus *Lumbricus,* the genus *Bimastos* (considered by Gates to be a North American taxon) also disappears from the British list.

Key to the adults of families of British earthworms

1. Clitellum, anterior margin *behind* segment *xix* (male pores preclitellar on *xv*, rarely *xiii*) ....Lumbricidae (p. 47)

   Clitellum, anterior margin *before* segment *xvii* (male pores intraclitellar or by the posterior margin of the clitellum) **2**

2. Setae numerous around the equator of each segment, i.e. perichaetine (Fig. D) .... Megascolecidae (p. 126)

   Setae, eight (four pairs) on each segment, i.e. lumbricine (Fig.7A–C) **3**

3. Setal pairs on the caudal region widely and closely paired on alternate segments, i.e. quincunx (*Pontoscolex*) ....
   .... Glossoscolecidae (p. 123)

   Setal pairs, distance apart regular throughout body **4**

4. Male pores inconspicuous on segment *xix*; "prostatic" pores separate, inconspicuous, paired on several segments; clitellum extending back to segments *xxvi* or *xxvii* ......Sparganophilidae (p. 120)

   Male pores conspicuous on segment *xvii* or *xviii* combined with prostatic pores, or, on segment *xviii* with paired prostatic pores on segments *xvii* and *xix*; clitellum seldom extending behind segment *xx* **5**

5. Female and spermathecal pores combined, single large pair on segment *xiv (Eudrilus)* .... Eudrilidae (p. 145)

   Female pores inconspicuous, paired on segment *xiv*; spermathecal pores inconspicuous paired in furrows 7/8 and/or 8/9 .... **6**

6. Excretory system micronephridial .... Octochaetidae (p. 142)

   Excretory system meganephridial **7**

7. Prostatic pores paired on segments *xvii* and *xix*, male pores paired on segment *xviii* .... Ocnerodrilidae (part) (p. 138)

   Prostatic and male pores paired, combined or close together on segment *xvii* **8**

8. Male pores at the posterior margin of the clitellum; dorsal pores absent (*Microscolex*)................................. Acanthodrilidae (p. 140)

   Male pores intraclitellar; dorsal pores present ....
   .... Ocnerodrilidae (part) (p. 138)

Family LUMBRICIDAE Rafinesque-Schmaltz, 1815

Body usually cylindrical sometimes with the posterior region depressed or infrequently body quadrangular, octagonal or trapezoidal in cross-section. Dorsal pores present, exceptionally (Diporodrilinae) replaced by paired, intersegmental, laterodorsal coelomic pores. Setae 4 pairs on each segment. Clitellum usually saddle-shaped occupying 4–32 segments between segments *xvii–lii*; paired tubercula pubertatis present, band-like or papillate. Male pores moderate to large, paired usually on segment *xv*, rarely on *xiii* or *xiv* (*Eiseniella*), occasionally inconspicuous and intraclitellar *circa* segment *xxvii* (*Fitzingeria* spp., *Orodrilus* spp.); prostatic pores absent. Spermathecal pores paired, inconspicuous in 2 to 8 furrows between 5/6 to 19/20 located anywhere between setal line *a* to near the mid-dorsal line (commonly 2 pairs in furrows 9/10/11 between setal lines *cd*). Oesophageal gizzard absent; single intestinal gizzard present in one segment (Lumbricinae) or in two segments (Diporodrilinae) in segments *xvii–xx*, preceded by a crop in a single segment; calciferous glands internal (intra-mural) in the wall of the oesophagus in one or more segments between (*ix*) *x–xv*. Prostates or prostate-like glands absent. Spermathecae adiverticulate, either interparietal or extending freely into the coelom. Meganephridial.

Notes: A family inhabiting forest litters and a wide range of soil types, indigenous to the central Holarctic. Following transportation, a few species have become established in most temperate regions of the world. The subfamily Diporodrilinae is confined to Corsica.

Key to the adults of British Lumbricidae

1. Setae behind clitellum closely paired (Fig. 7A)......................... **2**

   Setae behind clitellum widely paired or distant (Fig. 7B, C).......... **16**

2. Prostomium tanylobous.. **3**

   Prostomium not tanylobous... **7**

3. Clitellum with anterior margin before segment *xxvi*; tubercula pubertatis absent......................................*Lumbricus eiseni* (p. 98)

   Clitellum with anterior margin on or behind segment *xxvi*; tubercula pubertatis paired on four segments......................... **4**

4. Male pores inconspicuous; tubercula pubertatis with posterior pair on or before segment *xxxii* **5**

   Male pores seen as transverse slits with raised tumid lips; tubercula pubertatis with anterior pair on or behind segment *xxxiii* **6**

5. Tubercula pubertatis on segments *xxviii–xxxi* ....
   ....*Lumbricus rubellus* (p. 104)

   Tubercula pubertatis on segments *xxix–xxxii* ....
   ....*Lumbricus castaneus* (p. 96)

48

6(4) Tubercula pubertatis on segments *xxxiii–xxxvi* ....
.... *Lumbricus terrestris* (p. 106)

Tubercula pubertatis on segments *xxxiv–xxxvii*, papillate on *xxxiv* and *xxxvi*............................... *Lumbricus friendi* (p. 102)

Tubercula pubertatis on segments *xxxv–xxxviii* ....
.... *Lumbricus festivus* (p. 100)

7(2) Male pores on segment *xiii*; body behind clitellum quadrangular in cross section................................. *Eiseniella tetraedra* (p. 90)

Male pores on segment *xv*; body behind clitellum never quadrangular in cross section 8

8. Tubercula pubertatis absent or beginning on or before segment *xxix* 9

Tubercula pubertatis beginning on or behind segment *xxx* 13

9. Male pore tumescences confined to segment *xv* 10

Male pore tumescences extend onto or across segments *xiv–xvi* 12

10. Tubercula pubertatis on segments *xxix–xxxii*..........................
.... *Aporrectodea rosea* (p. 65)

Tubercula pubertatis on segments *xxviii–xxx*.......................... 11

Tubercula pubertatis absent or on segments *xxvi–xxx* .....*see* footnote*

11. Dorsal surface brown-red, pigment often absent from furrows, colour otherwise yellowish white ...... *Eisenia fetida* (p. 80)

Body uniformly pigmented a dark, brownish red ....
.... *Eisenia andrei* (p. 79)

---

* The North American earthworm *Bimastos parvus* will key out here. Gates (1956:7) recorded this species in soil with plants imported from 'England' and 'Wales' intercepted by officers of the Division of Plant Quarantine, New York in 1949. It was previously included in the British list on a single dubious record from Dublin when variations in the morphology of this species and of *Lumbricus eiseni* with which it was confused, were less well known (Gerard, 1964:35).

Diagnosis of *Bimastos parvus* (Eisen, 1874): Length 17–85 mm, diameter 1.5–4 mm, segments 65–110. Body cylindrical. Pigmented, reddish purple above, yellowish below. Prostomium epilobous. First dorsal pore (4/5) 5/6. Spermathecal pores absent. Male pores with small tumescences extending 14/15–15/16. Clitellum (*xxiii*) (*xxiv*) (*xxv*) *xxvi–xxx* (*xxxi*) (*xxxii*) (*xxxiii*). Tubercula pubertatis commonly absent, occasionally seen as an ill-defined ridge along the borders of the clitellum especially (*xxvi*) (*xxvii*) *xxviii, xxix* (*xxx*). Setae closely paired, post-clitellar formula $aa:ab:bc:cd:dd = 3:1.1:2.5:1:10$. Genital tumescences not known to surround setae.

A woodland species preferring moist situations such as moss, decaying wood and leaves; also known from compost. A North American species now introduced into several countries of western Europe and into Australia and New Zealand; always rare, e.g. in France known only from two records (Bouché, 1972:386).

12(9)   Tubercula pubertatis on segments *xxix* and *xxx*; first dorsal pore
furrow 4/5 .... *Helodrilus oculatus* (p. 94)

Tubercula pubertatis absent or as marginal thickenings of the
clitellum on segments *xxix–xxxi*; first dorsal pore furrow
(11/12) 12/13 .... *Murchieona minuscula* (p. 109)

13(8)   Tubercula pubertatis, anterior pair behind segment *xxxiv* ....
.... *Aporrectodea icterica* (p. 58)

Tubercula pubertatis, anterior pair before segment *xxxiv* **14**

14.   Tubercula pubertatis as sucker-like discs on segments *xxxi*,
xxxiii and *xxv* .... *Allolobophora chlorotica* (p. 50)

Tubercula pubertatis ridge-like or papillate, posterior pair on
segment *xxxiii* or *xxxiv* **15**

15.   Tubercula pubertatis on segments *xxxi* (*xxxii*) *xxxiii* ....
.... *Aporrectodea caliginosa* (p. 54)

Tubercula pubertatis on segments (*xxxi*) *xxxii–xxxiv* ....
.... *Aporrectodea longa* (p. 62)

Tubercula pubertatis on segments *xxxiii* and *xxxiv* ....
.... *Aporrectodea limicola* (p. 60)

16(1)   Male pore tumescences confined to segment *xv* (rarely extending across one furrow) **17**

Male pore tumescences extend across (both) furrows 14/15 and
15/16 ....   **19**

17.   Tubercula pubertatis absent or on segments (*xxviii*) *xxix, xxx* ...
.... *Dendrodrilus rubidus* (p. 76)

Tubercula pubertatis on segments *xxx* and *xxxi* **18**

Tubercula pubertatis on segments *xxx–xxxii* ....
.... *Dendrobaena attemsi* (p. 68)

Tubercula pubertatis on segments *xxx–xxxiii* ....
.... *Octolasion cyaneum* (p. 112)

Tubercula pubertatis on segments *xxxi–xxxiii* ....
.... *Dendrobaena octaedra* (p. 70)

Tubercula pubertatis on segments (*xxxiv*) *xxxv, xxxvi* (*xxxvii*)
.... *Dendrobaena pygmaea* (p. 73)

18.   Body length over 50 mm; pigmentation often transversely
striped .... *Eisenia veneta* (p. 88)

Body length less than 50 mm; pigmentation more or less
uniform above .... *Eisenia hortensis* (p. 84)

19(16) Tubercula pubertatis on segments *xxx–xxxv* ....
.... *Octolasion t. tyrtaeum* (p. 115)

Tubercula pubertatis on segments *xxxiii, xxxiv* ....
.... *Satchellius mammalis* (p. 118)

Genus ALLOLOBOPHORA Eisen, 1873

Calciferous sacs discharging posteriorly into the oesophagus of segment x, opening ventrally just in front of septum 10/11. Calciferous lamellae continued along lateral walls of sacs. Nephridial vesicles, J-shaped. Nephridiopores inconspicuous, alternating irregularly and with asymmetry on each side of the body anywhere above setal line b. Prostomium epilobous. Pigment, if present, *not* red.

Allolobophora chlorotica (Savigny)
(Fig. 12 and Front cover)

Enterion chloroticum Savigny, 1826:182.
Helodrilus (Allolobophora) chloroticus: Michaelsen, 1900:486.
Allolobophora chlorotica: Tétry, 1937:145; Gerard, 1964:30; Bouché, 1972:263; Gates, 1980:177.

Length 30–80 mm, diameter 3–7 mm, segment number 80–138. Body cylindrical, posterior region frequently depressed. Colour variable, dimorphic, pigmented dark green with younger individuals yellowish green (juveniles unpigmented) or unpigmented when flesh coloured.

Prostomium epilobous. First dorsal pore in furrow 4/5 (5/6). Spermathecal pores three pairs in furrows 8/9/10/11 in setal line c. Male pores on segment xv between setal lines bc with large tumescences extending over segments $\frac{1}{2}xiv-\frac{1}{2}xvi$. Clitellum covering segments ($xxviii$) $xxix-xxxvii$; saddle-shaped. Tubercula pubertatis seen as three pairs of small sucker-like papillae ventrally on segments $xxxi$, $xxxiii$ and $xxxv$, carried by paired narrow longitudinal bands extending from segment $xxx-xxxvi$ just laterally to setal lines b (Fig. 12(a)).

Setae closely paired, post-clitellar formula $aa:ab:bc:cd:dd = 13:1.5:6:1:25$. Genital tumescences around setae ab on segment ix (x, xi, $xxvii$, $xxix$, $xxxii$) and setae cd on segment x.

Septa 7/8/9 strong muscular, 5/6/7 and 10/11/12 less strongly thickened. Seminal vesicles, paired in four segments $ix-xii$.

Capsules: Length 2.2–4.1 mm, diameter 2.1–3.3 mm; usually spherical. Opaque, pale yellow with brownish poles, one usually with an umbrella-shaped membrane; surface smooth (Fig. 12(b)). Usually one hatchling emerges from each capsule; length 11 mm, unpigmented with a distinct white dorsal band immediately anterior to the crop.

Reproduction: Obligatory biparental; copulation in the soil. Spermatophores, up to ten on segments $xxvi-xxxix$. Chromosome number 32.

Habitat: Often numerically co-dominant with *Aporrectodea caliginosa* in cultivated soils and pastures; common in gardens and greenhouses, grassland, woodland under rotting logs and other vegetation (compost); occurs in ditches, river beds, among plant roots in lakes, wet highly organic soils,

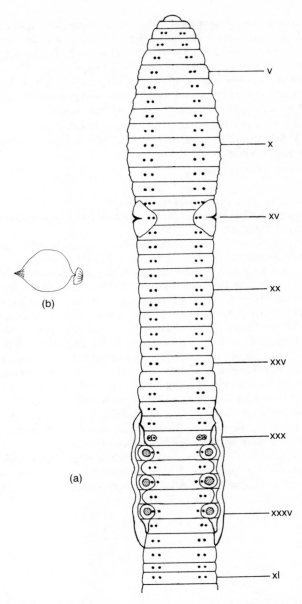

Fig. 12. *Allolobophora chlorotica*. (*a*) ventral view of the anterior region, (*b*) egg capsule.

marshes with decaying plant debris, banks of streams and lakes, estuarine flats, semi-fixed sand dunes and caves. Recorded from a wide variety of soil types, e.g. sand, clay and peaty soils with pH 4.5–8.2; usually within 60 mm of the surface of the soil among or near the roots of plants. The pigmented green phase is commoner in pasture and moist situations where it can be the dominant species, the unpigmented pink phase occurs mainly in gardens and woodlands especially in moderate to well-drained soils.

Distribution: Western Palaearctic and eastern North America, Greenland and North Atlantic islands introduced into New Zealand and temperate regions of South America.

British records: Widespread.

Notes:

(1) Known as the green or stubby worm.

(2) A copious yellow coelomic fluid is released from the dorsal pores when the worm is disturbed.

(3) Variations in the position of the clitellum, tubercula pubertatis and the number of spermathecae were recorded in France by Bouché (1972).

(4) Colour dimorphism is common; green morphs possess a bilin pigment which is lacking in the pink morphs. Each colour phase has its own ecological preferences and the colouration is unaffected by diet. The colour phases are genetically isolated; the pink condition is dominant over green and the heterozygous (laboratory bred hydrid) pink offsping are wholly or partially male sterile (Satchell, 1967). The relationship between the two colour phases seemingly parallels that between *Eisenia fetida* and *Eisenia andrei*. However, further research is required to determine the status of the two morphs. Should each come to be regarded as a separate species, then the green morphs will continue to be known as *chlorotica* and the name *virescens* Savigny, 1826 is available for the pink, unpigmented morph. Most of the records of these two morphs are confused so any differences in their distributions have been obscured.

(5) The cluster fly *Pollenia rudis* (F.) which aggregates in winter and may be a nuisance in buildings, has a parasitic larva occurring in several earthworm species including *Allolobophora chlorotica* (see p. 27).

Genus APORRECTODEA Örley, 1885

Calciferous sacs opening vertically into the equator of the oesophagus in segment x. Calciferous lamellae continued onto the posterior walls of the sacs. Nephridial vesicles, U-shaped. Nephridiopores, inconspicuous alternating irregularly and with asymmetry on each side of the body anywhere above setal line b. Prostomium epilobous. Pigment, if present, *not* red.

54

Aporrectodea caliginosa (Savigny)

(Figs 13 and 14)

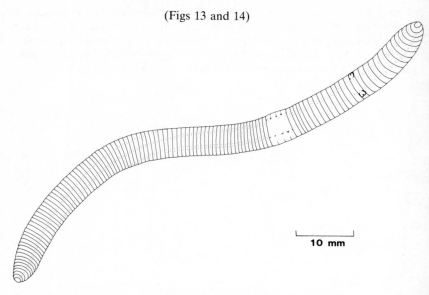

10 mm

Fig. 13. *Aporrectodea caliginosa*. Whole animal (drawn by Solene Morris).

Enterion caliginosum Savigny, 1826:180.
Helodrilus (*Allolobophora*) *caliginosus:* Michaelsen, 1900:482.
Allolobophora caliginosa: Tétry, 1937:146; Gerard, 1964:27; Zicsi, 1982:444.
Nicodrilus caliginosus caliginosus: Bouché, 1972:326.
Nicodrilus caliginosus alternisetosus Bouché, 1972:333.
Nicodrilus caliginosus meridionalis Bouché, 1972:334.
Lumbricus trapezoides Dugès, 1828:289.
Helodrilus (*Allolobophora*) *caliginosus trapezoides:* Michaelsen, 1900:483.
Allolobophora trapezoides: Gates, 1972b:2.
Allolobophora turgida Eisen, 1873; Gates, 1972b:89.
Allolobophora turgida tuberculata Eisen, 1874:43.
Allolobophora tuberculata: Gerard, 1964:30; Gates, 1972b:43.
Allolobophora nocturna Evans, 1946:98; Gerard, 1964:29; Gates, 1972b:134.
Nicodrilus nocturnus: Bouché, 1972:337.

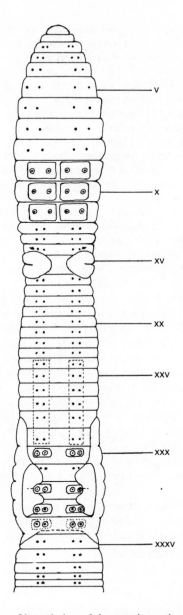

V

X

XV

XX

XXV

XXX

XXXV

Fig. 14. *Aporrectodea caliginosa*. Ventral view of the anterior region.

Length 40–180 mm, diameter 3.5–7 mm, segment number 120–246. Body cylindrical. Colour variable, polymorphic, from unpigmented pale pink anteriorly through whitish grey posteriorly in small individuals to pigmented dark reddish brown with the anterior dorsum almost purplish brown. Prostomium epilobous. First dorsal pore in furrow (6/7) 9/10–12/13 (14/15). Spermathecal pores in furrows 9/10/11 between setal lines *cd*. Male pores on segment *xv* above setal line *b* with tumescences usually encroaching on to the adjacent segments but seldom as far as $\frac{1}{2}xiv$–$\frac{1}{2}xvi$. Clitellum extends over at least six segments (*xxvii*) *xxxi–xxxiv* (*xxxv*); saddle-shaped. Tubercula pubertatis comprising basically two pairs on segments ($\frac{1}{2}xxx$) *xxxi–xxxiii* ($\frac{1}{2}xxxiv$) that may be confluent to form a simple ridge on each side or may be separated by a transverse furrow at $\frac{1}{2}xxxii$, occasionally papillate (Figs. 13 and 14(a)).

Setae closely paired, post-clitellar formula $aa : ab : bc : cd : dd = 4.5 : 1.5 : 3 : 1 : 15$. Genital tumescences surround setae *ab* on segments *ix–xi*(*xii*), sometimes *xxvi–xxix*, but invariably on some or all of segments *xxx, xxxii–xxxiv* (*xxxv–xxxvii*) (Figs. 13 and 14).

Septa 5/6–9/10 moderately thickened. Seminal vesicles paired in four segments, *ix–xii*.

Capsules: Length 2.8–9.2 mm, diameter 2.4–5.5 mm; lemon-shaped, cylindrical or spherical. Opaque, pale yellow often with brown stippling around the poles. Surface smooth. Hatchling length 12 mm.

Reproduction: Obligatory biparental; copulation mainly in the soil, only occasionally on the surface. Spermatophores often 1 or 2, usually over segments *xxv–xxxi*. Most capsules are produced during the spring and autumn. Chromosome number 36.

Habitat: Numerically dominant in gardens and most cultivated land including meadows; also occurs in the banks of streams, infrequently in litter or under compost. Present in alkaline soils with pH 5.9–11.1. Small individuals are common in the top 70 mm of the soil where they live in temporary horizontal burrows and occasionally make small casts on the surface of the soil. Larger individuals ("*nocturna*") become deep-borrowing and produce large surface casts.

Distribution: Western Palaearctic and eastern Nearctic, introduced into other temperate regions of the world mainly in cultivation, becoming established where native species have become locally extinct.

British records: Widespread.

Notes:
(1) Known as grey worm, turgid worm, trapeze worm.
(2) Until recently (Zicsi, 1982), this species was considered to form a species group containing several component taxa (Gates, 1972*b*). Four morphs were commonly recognized as separate species:

(a) *caliginosa* s.s (syn. *turgida*). Length 60–85 mm; colour pale pink anteriorly, whitish-grey posteriorly; tubercula pubertatis ridge-like over segments *xxxi–xxxiii* often bipartite being divided by a transverse furrow at ½*xxxii*, 120–150 body segments.

(b) *tuberculata*. Length 90–150 mm; colour mainly whitish grey perhaps with a brownish speckling; tubercula pubertatis extending over ½*xxx–*½*xxxiv* formed from two raised, somewhat triangular, areas with their apices in segments *xxxi* and *xxxiii* directed mid-ventrally; genital tumescences surround setae *ab* on segments *xxx, xxxii* and *xxxiv*, i.e. absent from segment *xxxiii*, 152–194 body segments.

(c) *nocturna*. Length 90–180 mm; colour dark reddish brown, more purplish anteriorly; tubercula pubertatis always as a bipartite ridge bisected by a transverse furrow at ½*xxxii*; genital tumescences surround setae *ab* on segments *xxix, xxx, xxxii–xxxiv*, 200–246 body segments.

(d) *trapezoides*. Length 80–140 mm; tubercula pubertatis poorly differentiated as papillae on segments *xxxi* and *xxxiii*, possibly linked by a narrow bridge in *xxxii*, i.e. tripartite; genital tumescences surround setae *ab* only on segments *xxxii–xxxiv*. Uniquely male sterile, spermatophores absent.

The variations in these four morphs are now considered to be mostly phenotypic with pigmentation and behaviour being a function of size with the larger, purplish worms living deeper in the soil. The varying development of the tubercula pubertatis and the genital tumescences seem largely to reflect increased sexual activity associated with large size. There are other factors, the morph *trapezoides* is noted for possessing massive infestations of the protozoan parasite of the male organs, *Monocystis*, consistent with its male sterility and the consequent absence of spermatophores. Since the colour of this morph is variable and includes all of the colours of the other morphs, worms identified as *trapezoides* could represent a pathological condition common to all phenotypes, see p. 44.

In addition to the comprehensive surveys of variation made by Gates (1972b), evidence of further diversity was reported among French populations by Bouché (1972). He recognized two new subspecies, *alternisetosa* which resembles the morph *tuberculata* and *meridionalis* which is similar to *trapezoides*, in addition to providing infrasubspecific names for other variants. Clearly this is a highly plastic species with many morphological variants occurring throughout its range. The numerous morphs however do not warrant taxonomic separation in view of their seemingly being no more than growth, pathological local phenotypic variants. Ecologists may wish to record "*nocturna*" separately when deep-burrowing and surface-casting activities of immature and adult worms influence their experimental results.

Aporrectodea icterica (Savigny)
(Fig. 15)

Enterion ictericum Savigny, 1826:182.
Helodrilus (*Helodrilus*) *ictericus:* Michaelsen, 1900:500.
Eophila icterica: Gerard, 1964:44.
Allolobophora icterica: Bouché, 1972:273.
Aporrectodea icterica: Reynolds, 1976:3; Reynolds, 1977:40.

Length 50–140 mm, diameter 3–6 mm, segment number (132) 150–170(200). Body cylindrical. Unpigmented; colour variable grey, brown or yellow. Prostomium epilobous. First dorsal pore in furrow 4/5 (5/6). Spermathecal pores, two or three pairs in furrows (8/9) 9/10/11 in setal line *c*. Male pores on segment *xv* located between setal lines *b* and *c* on small tumescences usually encroaching onto the adjacent segments and may extend between ½*xiv*–½*xvi*. Clitellum longer and located more posteriorly than in other British species, extending over segments (*xxxiii*) *xxxiv–xlii* (*xliii*), (*xliv*); saddle-shaped. Tubercula pubertatis seen as narrow bands, often poorly demarcated, along the ventral borders of the clitellum over segments (*xxxv*) *xxxvi–xlii* (*xliii*), about midway between setal lines *b* and *c* (Fig. 15).

Setae closely paired, post-clitellar formula *aa*:*ab*:*bc*:*cd*:*dd* = 9:1:5:1:30. Genital tumescences occasionally surround setae *ab* on segments *xi–xiv* and the clitellar segments, also sometimes setae *cd* on segments *ix* (*x*) (*xi*) (Fig. 15).

Capsules: Not recorded.

Reproduction. Details unknown, seemingly obligatory biparental. Chromosome number 32.

Habitat: Known in Britain only from cultivation or nearby with records from gardens, orchards, and meadow (agricultural research station). Common locally.

Distribution: Denmark, western Germany, Belgium, France, Switzerland, northern Italy and Portugal. Introduced into United States (New York) and Canada (Ontario).

British records: Introduced: Cambridge, Kew and Oxford botanic gardens, Hertfordshire (Rothamsted) and Central Scotland (Stirling) at agricultural research stations also sporadically in cultivation in Essex (Bradwell-on-Sea), Gwynedd (Talyllyn), Staffordshire (Edgbaston), Suffolk (Brandon), Surrey (Purley) and Co. Down, Eire (Redburn).

Notes:
(1) Known as the mottled worm.
(2) The original home of the species is unknown. Apart from Portugal, the species has been recorded only from areas glaciated during the Quaternary (Cotton, 1979).

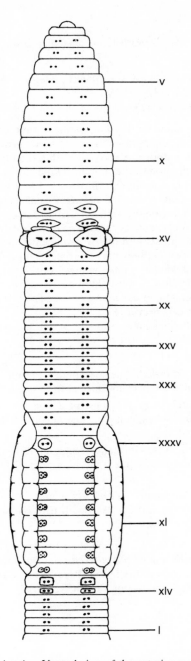

Fig. 15. *Aporrectodea icterica*. Ventral view of the anterior region.

Aporrectodea limicola (Michaelsen)
(Fig. 16)

Allolobophora limicola Michaelsen, 1890:10, Gates, 1957:1; Gerard, 1964:31; Gates, 1972*b*:113.
Helodrilus (*Allolobophora*) *limicolus:* Michaelsen, 1900:484.

Length 40–100 mm, diameter 3–4 mm, segment number 86–146. Body cylindrical with somewhat enlarged anterior segments giving a swollen appearance. Unpigmented, anterior region pink with the remaining segments more greyish in colour. Prostomium epilobous. First dorsal pore in furrow 4/5 (5/6). Spermathecal pores paired in furrows 9/10/11 between setal lines *cd*.
Male pores on segment *xv* located between setal lines *b* and *c* on distinct tumescences that occasionally extend across furrows 14/15 and 15/16.
Clitellum occurs over segments (*xxviii*) *xxix–xxxv* (*xxxvi*); saddle-shaped.
Tubercula pubertatis present on the two adjacent segments *xxxiii* and *xxxiv* between setal lines *b* and *c*; they may be somewhat papillate or tend towards a continuous ridge divided by a fine shallow groove at furrow 33/34 (Fig. 16).
Setae closely paired, post-clitellar formula, *aa* : *ab* : *bc* : *cd* : *dd* = 6 : 1.2 : 4 : 1 : 19. Genital tumescences carry setae *ab* on some or all of segments *ix–xiv, xvi–xvii* and *xxv–xxxviii* (Fig. 16).
Septa 6/7/8/9/10 thickened. Seminal vesicles paired in four segments *ix–xii*.

Capsules: Not recorded.

Reproduction: Not recorded. Spermatophore present ventrally by furrow 31/32 on the specimen from Hampshire. Chromosome number 36.

Habitat: Known mainly from marshes, peat bogs and other wet soils only occasionally found in ditches, damp pasture and arable land; soil pH 3.7–7.0. Rare.

Distribution: Sweden, West Germany, Switzerland, Belgium, Britain. Introduced into the United States (Georgia, New Jersey, Oregon, Pennsylvania and Washington).

British records: Hampshire (Furzley), Cumbria (Grange-over-Sands), Dumfries (Forest of Ae) and Co. Wexford, Eire (Johnstown Castle).

Notes:
This species may be more common than the few records would suggest, due possibly to confusion with *Aporrectodea caliginosa*. The original home of the species is unknown; the few scattered European records come from areas that were glaciated during the Quaternary.

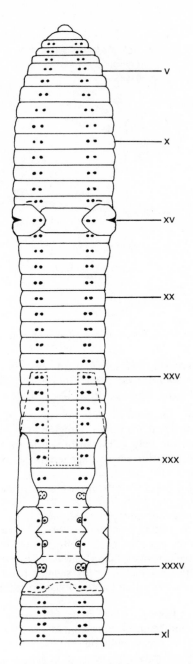

Fig. 16. *Aporrectodea limicola*. Ventral view of the anterior region.

Aporrectodea longa (Ude)
(Figs. 17 and 18)

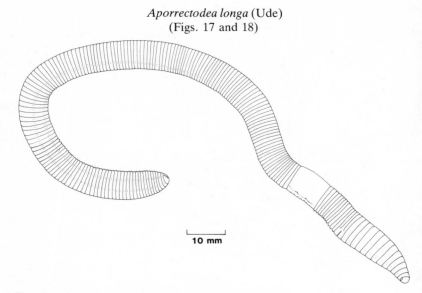

Fig. 17. *Aporrectodea longa*. Whole animal (drawn by Solene Morris).

Allolobophora longa Ude, 1885:136; Gerard, 1964:28; Gates, 1972b:114.
Helodrilus (*Allolobophora*) *longus:* Michaelsen, 1900:483.
Nicodrilus longus longus: Bouché, 1972:322.

Length 90–170 mm, diameter 4–9 mm, segment number (146) 170–190 (222). Body cylindrical with the posterior region somewhat depressed. Lightly pigmented, colour from pale yellowish brown to dark reddish brown with the dorsum of the anterior region being darkest; slight greenish orange iridescence dorsally.

Prostomium epilobous. First dorsal pore in furrow (9/10) 12/13 (14/15). Spermathecal pores, two pairs in furrows 9/10/11, located slightly above setal line *c*. Male pores on segment *xv* situated between setal lines *b* and *c* with tumescences extending from furrow 14/15 to furrow 15/16 and occasionally beyond to the equators of segments *xiv* and *xvi*. Clitellum covering eight or nine segments over (*xxvii*) *xxviii–xxxv* (*xxxvi*); saddle-shaped. Tubercula pubertatis (*xxxi*) *xxxii–xxxiv*, seen as band-like, low oval ridges laterally to setal line *b* but often broad enough to reach setal line *c* (Figs. 17 and 18a).

Setae closely paired, post-clitellar formula $aa:ab:bc:cd:dd = 12:1.5:6:1:20$. Genital tumescences around setae *ab* on segments *ix, x, xi* and *xxxi, xxxiii, xxxiv*; occasionally on other segments (*see below*, 'Notes').

Septa 7/8/9 only are muscular. Seminal vesicles paired in four segments, *ix–xii*.

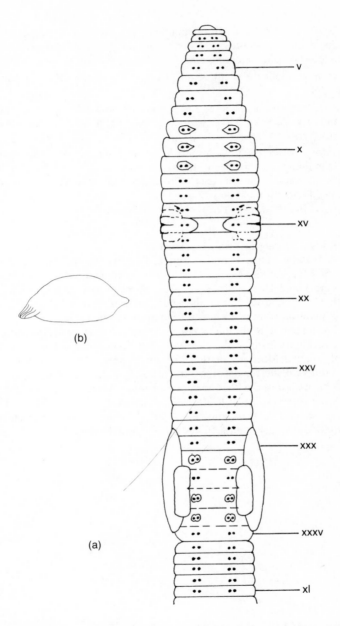

V

X

XV

XX

XXV

XXX

(b)

(a)

XXXV

xl

Fig. 18. *Aporrectodea longa*. (*a*) ventral view of the anterior region, (*b*) egg capsule.

Capsules: Length 4.4–7.9 mm, diameter 3.3–5.2 mm. Colour pale yellow darkening to green or brown at the poles; opaque with a smooth surface (Fig. 18b). Only one hatchling emerges from each capsule, length 27 mm.

Reproduction: Obligatory biparental. Copulation in the soil. Chromosome number 36.

Habitat: Common in gardens and cultivated soils also in pastures and woodlands especially with loamy or chalk soils, pH 6.7–9.4; numerous in the banks of rivers and lakes.

Distribution: Widespread in northern temperate regions: Palaearctic region from Scandinavia to northern Italy then eastwards to Siberia, in North America principally in the east; introduced into (?) Mexico, Australia (including Tasmania) and New Zealand.

British records: Widespread.

Notes:

(1) Known as long-worm or blackhead.

(2) In Britain casting is more abundant during the two main periods of activity, March until May (or later if the soil remains moist) and between September and December. Permanent burrows may be constructed to a depth of 400–600 mm, their presence being indicated by large casts of faecal material comprising waste food and soil piled around the entrance.

(3) This species and the rarer '*nocturna*' phase of *Aporrectodea caliginosa* are difficult to distinguish, especially the juveniles which are separable mainly on the locations of the first dorsal pores and differences in the comparative distances between setae *aa* and *bc*. In France this species has often been confused with *Aporrectodea giardi* Ribaucourt, 1901 (formerly known erroneously as '*Allolobophora terrestris* (Savigny, 1826)'). The French species is now known to differ, among other characters, by additionally having genital tumescences around setae *ab* on segments *xii* and *xxx*.

Aporrectodea rosea (Savigny)
(Fig. 19)

Enterion roseum Savigny, 1826:182.
Eisenia rosea: Michaelsen, 1900:478; Tétry, 1937:143; Gates, 1974c:9;
Reynolds, 1977:78.
Allolobophora rosea: Pop, 1948:69; Gerard, 1964:32; Bouché, 1972:418.
Aporrectodea rosea: Gates, 1976:4.
Allolobophora rosea macedonica Rosa, 1893:428; Gerard, 1964:33.
Eisenia rosea macedonica: Michaelson, 1900:479.

Length 25–85 mm, diameter 2–6 mm, segment number (104) 120–140 (165).
Body predominantly cylindrical but the ventral surface of the clitellum is
flattened while the posterior region is frequently depressed; the periproct is
bluntly rounded, never pointed. (When the worm is irritated, the anterior
region becomes blunt, almost bulbous, and white coelomic fluid is expelled.)
Unpigmented with at least the region anterior to the crop a clear rosy pink
and the remainder of the body pale pink or pinkish grey, the clitellum may be
pale yellow, orange or brown.

Prostomium epilobous. First dorsal pore in furrow 4/5 (5/6), large.

Spermathecal pores, two pairs present located dorsally in furrows 9/10/11,
about three-quarters of the distance from setal line d to the mid-dorsum.
Male pores on segment xv lie between setal lines b and c with the
tumescences usually confined to segment xv or possibly encroaching slightly
onto xvi. Clitellum extends over segments (xxv) $xxvi–xxxii$ $(xxxiii)$ frequently
with the posterior segments (those carrying the tubercula pubertatis) broader
than the anterior segments; saddle-shaped. Tubercula pubertatis over segments $xxix–xxxi$ seen as continuous bands, often protuberant, extending
laterally to setal line b (Fig. 19a).

Setae closely paired, post-clitellar formula $aa:ab:bc:cd:dd =$
$12:1.5:6:1:29$. Genital tumescences carry both setal pairs ab and cd on
segments ix and xi (perhaps also on segments x, xii and $xiii$) while additional
tumescences may carry setae ab in the clitellar region especially on segments
$xxvi–xxxii$ (Fig. 19a).

Septa 6/7/8/9/10 strongly muscular, septa 10/11/12/13/14 (14/15) with
less muscularity. Seminal vesicles paired commonly in four segments, $ix–xii$
but the two anterior pairs may be reduced or absent.

Capsules: Length 2.5–3.6 mm, diameter 2.1–3.4 mm. Opaque with smooth
surface, colour pale yellow becoming brown at the poles (Fig. 19b). One
hatchling emerges from each capsule, length 12 mm.

Reproduction: Biparental reproduction unknown, seemingly
parthenogenetic. Chromosome number basically 54 (3n = 54), polyploidy
common (*not* recorded in Britain) when the chromosome number may be
72, 90, 108, 160–174. The chromosome number of 53 (3n − 1) has been
reported in *macedonica*, now regarded as a junior synonym (Pop, 1948).

Habitat: Most habitats with pH 4.9–9.8: in soil, under leaves, stones and logs in pastures, gardens and woodlands; in limnic situations on the banks of rivers and lakes; recorded from caves and greenhouses.

Distribution: Western Palaearctic and Nearctic, introduced into South America, South Africa and Australasia.

British records: Widely distributed. Common.

Notes:

(1) Known as rosy (-tip) worm, mucous worm.

(2) Polymorphism associated with polyploidy is common locally. Modifications occur mainly in the male reproductive systems, particularly in the reduction in the number of pairs of seminal vesicles (Bouché, 1972). Preserved specimens in which the colouration has been lost and with poorly developed tubercula pubertatis, may be confused with *small* individuals of *Eisenia fetida*. In addition to the internal generic characters, the species can be separated on external cahracters. In *rosea* the dorsal pores are large (small in *fetida*), the setal distance *aa* is twice the length of *bc* (in *fetida aa = bc*), the prostomium is clearly epilobous (in *fetida* it often tends towards the tanylobic condition) while the male pore tumesence usually encroaches onto segment *xvi* (in *fetida* the tumescence is confined to *xv*).

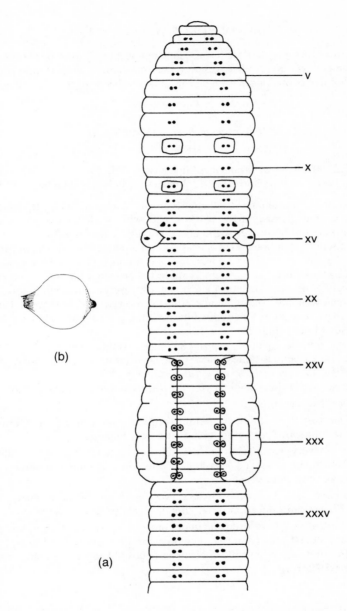

V

X

XV

XX

(b)

XXV

XXX

XXXV

(a)

Fig. 19. *Aporrectodea rosea*. (*a*) ventral view of the anterior region, (*b*) egg capsule.

Genus DENDROBAENA Eisen, 1873

Calciferous sacs absent. Calciferous gland opens directly into the oesophagus in segment *xi*. Nephridial vesicles ocarina-shaped with ventral ducts. Nephridiopores obvious in a single row along each side of the body. Pigment red.

Dendrobaena attemsi (Michaelsen)
(Fig. 20)

Helodrilus (Dendrobaena) attemsi Michaelsen, 1902:47.
Dendrobaena attemsi: Bouché, 1972:393; Gates, 1974b:54; Fender, 1982:8.

Length 26–70 mm, diameter 1–3 mm, segment number 125–145. Body cylindrical. Colour dorsally rosy to dark red with a characteristic, opaque (whitish) area at least over segments *ix–xi* (*xii*), ventrally paler.

Prostomium epilobous. First dorsal pore small, location variable in furrow (4/5/6/7) 7/8. Spermathecal pores, two pairs in furrows 9/10/11 in setal line *d*. Male pores paired on segment *xv* midway between setal lines *b* and *c*; on tumescences usually confined to segment *xv*, rarely encroaching onto ½*xvi*. Clitellum extending over segments (*xxviii*) *xxix–xxxiv*; saddle-shaped. Tubercula pubertatis seen as longitudinal narrow ridges across segments *xxx–xxxii* along setal line *b* (Fig. 20).

Setae widely paired, post-clitellar formula $aa:ab:bc:cd:dd = 1.2:1:1:1:2$. Genital tumescences sometimes around setae *a* and/or *b* on segments *ix–xi, xvi* (*xxiii–xxvi*) *xxviii–xxxiii* (Fig. 20).

Anterior septa thin. Seminal vesicles paired in four segments, *ix–xii*.

Capsules: Not recorded.

Reproduction: Presumably biparental (brilliant iridescence from sperm on the male funnels). Spermatophores found near male pores.

Habitat: In very acid situations (pH 3.5–5.6) in sandy and peaty soils, in woodland under moss and logs and in litter, in a greenhouse potting mix containing sphagnum peat.

Distribution: USSR, Czechoslovakia, Austria, Yugoslavia, Germany, Belgium, France; introduced into the United States (Oregon). Rare.

British record: Single record from under moss covering limestone in low, thin woodland near Cark, Cumbria; 1 September 1981 by A. Zicsi and R. W. Sims (6 adult and 3 juvenile specimens deposited in the British Museum (Natural History)).

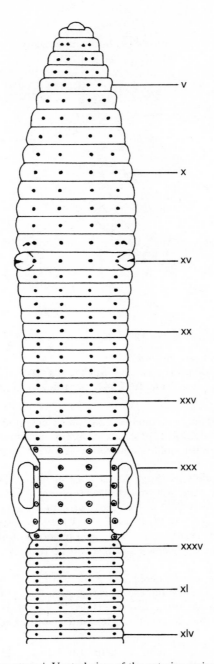

Fig. 20. *Dendrobaena attemsi*. Ventral view of the anterior region.

Dendrobaena octaedra (Savigny)
(Figs. 21 and 22)

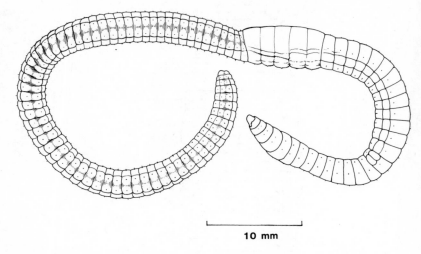

10 mm

Fig. 21. *Dendrobaena octaedra.* Whole animal (drawn by Mandy Holloway).

Enterion octaedrum Savigny, 1826:183.
Helodrilus (*Dendrobaena*) *octaedrus:* Michaelsen, 1900:494.
Dendrobaena octaedra: Tétry, 1937:144; Gerard, 1964:37; Bouché, 1972:388; Gates, 1974*b*:16.

Length (17) 30–40 (60) mm, diameter 2–5 mm, segment number (70) 90–105. Body anteriorly cylindrical, post-clitellar region octagonal in cross section. Colour red or reddish violet to brown or yellowish brown with a coppery iridescence.

Prostomium epilobous. First dorsal pore in furrow (4/5) 5/6. Spermathecal pores three pairs in furrows 9/10/11 in setal line *d*. Male pores paired on segment *xv* across setal line *b*, each carried on a small tumescence that may extend from furrow 14/15 to 15/16. Clitellum restricted to segments (*xxvii*) *xxviii, xxix–xxxiii, xxxiv*. Tubercula pubertatis form a narrow, often indistinct, band across segments *xxxi–xxxiii* (*xxxiv*) just above setal line *b* (Fig. 22a).

Setae distant, post-clitellar setal formula $aa:ab:bc:cd:dd =$ 1:1:1.2:1.2:1.8. Genital tumescences sometimes around setae *ab* on some or all of segments *xii, xvi, xxix–xxxiii* (Figs. 21 and 22a).

Anterior septa thin. Seminal vesicles paired in three segments, *ix, xi* and *xii*.

Capsules: Length 1.6–3.1 mm, diameter 1.6–2.2 mm. Opaque, whitish hue with brown coloured poles; surface smooth (Fig. 22b).

71

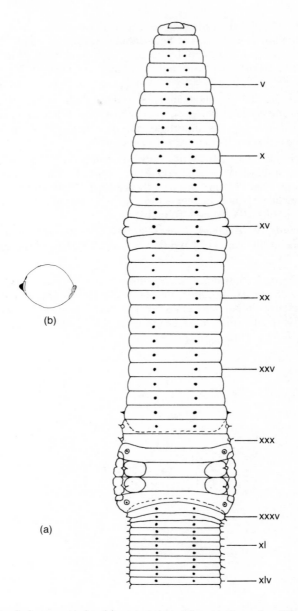

Fig. 22. *Dendrobaena octaedra*. (*a*) ventral view of the anterior region, (*b*) egg capsule.

Reproduction: Seeming parthenogenetic morphs have mostly been recorded as spermatophores have usually been absent; biparental (diploid) populations may exist as spermatophores were recorded in individuals from Greenland and Portugal. Chromosome number variable, 120–130, due to polyploidy.

Habitat: Recorded from under moss, woodland litter, rotting tree-stumps, sheep dung and wrack (sea-weed); associated with soils having a high organic content such as peat, wet moorland, forested and acid hill pasture (pH 3.3–7.7); occasionally limnic.

Distribution: Western Holarctic: Novaya Zemlya (73° N), Scandinavia, Greenland, Labrador, Washington State south to the Tyrrhenian and Adriatic alps (900–2000 m) through Switzerland, France and Portugal to Madeira in the east and to Mexico in the west. Introduced into southern India (Palni Hills 2100 m) and Colombia.

British records: Widespread: from Outer Hebrides in the north to Clare Island (Eire) in the west, to Guernsey (Channel Islands) in the south.

Notes:

Parthenogenetic polymorphism is considered to be widespread (Gates, 1974*b*) with up to 12 major morphs being recognized at a single site. Amphimictic, diploid individuals possibly occur since specimens with four pairs of seminal vesicles have been found in the Urals, USSR.

73

Dendrobaena pygmaea (Savigny)
(Fig. 23)

Enterion pygmaeum Savigny, 1826:183.
Helodrilus (Dendrobaena) pygmaeus: Michaelsen, 1900:495.
Dendrobaena pygmaea: Gerard, 1964:37; Gates, 1975c:8.
Dendrobaena pygmaea pygmaea: Bouché, 1972:393.
Allolobophora minima Rosa, 1884:39 (non Muldal, 1952).
Helodrilus (Eophila) cognettii Michaelsen, 1903:140 [nom. nov. pro
    Helodrilus (Helodrilus) ribaucourti Cognetti, 1901:21 (non Bretscher,
    1901)].
Dendrobaena pygmaea cognettii: Bouché, 1972:391.
Dendrobaena cognettii: Zicsi, 1981:171.

Length (15) 20–35 (45) mm, diameter 0.5–1.2 mm, segment number 90–110.
Body cylindrical, gradually tapering posteriorly. Colour: lightly pigmented
when red to reddish purple anteriorly mainly on the dorsum, or unpigmented
when more greyish in colour.

Prostomium epilobous. Dorsal pores inconspicuous beginning in furrow
(4/5) 5/6 (6/7), usually absent. Spermathecal pores three pairs opening
dorsally in furrows 9/10/11/12, frequently absent. Male pores paired on
segment xv between setal lines b and c, each carried on a conspicuous whitish
coloured tumescence confined to the segment perhaps not extending fully
from furrow 14/15 to furrow 15/16. Clitellum covers segments (xxxii)
xxxiii–xxxvii (xxxviii); saddle-shaped. Tubercula pubertatis usually absent,
when present they form an indistinct rectangular ridge below setal line b in
segments xxxv–xxxvii where they are interrupted by indistinct intersegmental
furrows (Fig. 23).

Setae distant, post-clitellar formula aa:ab:bc:cd:dd = 1.5:1.2:1.1:1:2.
Sometimes absent ventrally in the clitellar segments. Genital tumescences
unknown around setae (Fig. 23).

Anterior septa thin and membranous. Two pairs of seminal vesicles
sometimes present in segments xi and xii, often rudimentary or absent.

Capsules: Not recorded.

Reproduction: Not recorded, seemingly uniparental (?parthenogenetic) at
least in western Europe.

Habitat: Well-drained soil and moist litter, mossy banks of streams in
deciduous woodlands.

Distribution: Hungary, Germany, Italy also Sardinia, Spain, France and
Britain.

British records: Cumbria (south of Esthwaite Water), North Devon (Heddon
Valley), Hampshire (Ampfield) and Suffolk (Ramsholt).

Notes:

A poorly known species, originally imperfectly defined which has subsequently led to controversy about its correct name. Difficulties have arisen because of its variability being connected largely with the parthenogenesis prevalent among western European populations. (Bouché, 1972, recognized *pygmaea* as the rare amphimictic phase and *cognettii* as the commoner parthenogenetic phase lacking dorsal pores, seminal vesicles and spermathecae.) Despite nomenclative reservations, there is no doubt about the identity of this taxon in comparison with other members of the genus. We can, therefore, accept the interpretation of Michaelsen (1900) and regard this author as the first reviser to 'fix' the species when he provided a full description (*see* p. 44).

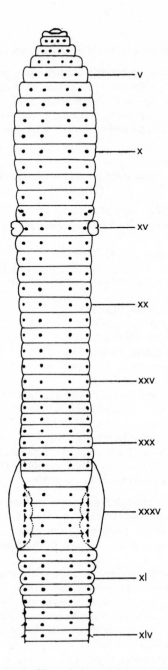

Fig. 23. *Dendrobaena pygmaea*. Ventral view of the anterior region.

Genus DENDRODRILUS Omodeo, 1956

Calciferous sacs opening posteriorly into the oesophagus ventrally just in front of septum 10/11. Calciferous lamellae continued anteriorly along the lateral walls of the sacs. Nephridial vesicles form a U-shaped loop. Nephridiopores, inconspicuous alternating irregularly and with asymmetry on each side of the body above setal line *b*. Prostomium epilobous. Pigment red.

Dendrodrilus rubidus (Savigny)
(Fig. 24)

Enterion rubidum Savigny, 1826:182.
Helodrilus (*Dendrobaena*) *rubidus:* Michaelsen, 1900:490 (syn. *tenuis* Eisen, 1874).
Dendrobaena rubida: Støp-Bovitz, 1969:220.
Dendrobaena rubida rubida: Gerard, 1964:40; Zicsi, 1982:443.
Dendrobaena (*Dendrodrilus*) *rubida rubida:* Bouché, 1972:410 (syn. *norvegica* Eisen, 1874).
Dendrodrilus rubidus: Gates, 1979:152.
Allolobophora norvegica Eisen, 1874:48.
Helodrilus norvegicus: Michaelsen, 1900:504.
Dendrobaena norvegica: Støp-Bovitz, 1969:230.
Dendrobaena rubida norvegica: Zicsi, 1982:443.
Allolobophora tenuis Eisen, 1874:44.
Dendrobaena rubida tenuis: Gerard, 1964:41; Zicsi, 1982:443.
Dendrobaena (*Dendrodrilus*) *rubida tenuis:* Bouché, 1972:411.
Allolobophora subrubicunda Eisen, 1874:51.
Dendrobaena subrubicunda: Støp-Bovitz, 1969:224.
Dendrobaena (*Dendrodrilus*) *subrubicunda:* Bouché, 1972:414.
Helodrilus (*Dendrobaena*) *rubidus subrubicundus:* Michaelsen, 1900:490.
Dendrobaena rubida subrubicunda: Gerard, 1964:40; Zicsi, 1982:443.

Length 20–100 mm, diameter 2–5 mm, segment number 50–120. Body cylindrical. Colour dark red, pale ventrally; polymorphic often pale red or pink with conspicuous yellow or orange posterior region caused by the accumulation of yellowish coloured waste products in the coelom of the last three to eight segments.

Prostomium epilobous. Dorsal pores inconspicuous, beginning in furrow 5/6. Spermathecal pores, when present, two pairs in furrows 9/10/11 slightly above setal line *c*. Male pores paired on segment *xv* between setal lines *b* and *c* with an oval tumescence varying from small and confined to segment *xv* to large and encroaching onto segments *xiv* and *xvi* but not obliterating furrows 14/15 and 15/16. Clitellum covers four to six segments, (*xxv*) *xxvi*, *xxvii–xxxi* (*xxxii*). Tubercula pubertatis present along the ventral borders of the clitellum in segments *xxviii–xxx* or only *xxix–xxx*; either as a broad,

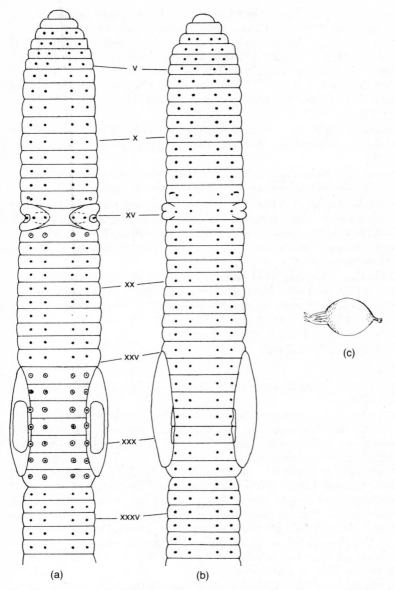

Fig. 24. *Dendrodrilus rubidus*. Ventral view of the anterior region. (*a*) *subrubicundus* morph, (*b*) *rubidus/tenuis* morph and (*c*) egg capsule.

rectangular band or reduced to a slender strip (when over two segments) and interrupted by furrow 29/30; occasionally absent (Fig. 24a and b).

Setae widely paired, post-clitellar setal formula approximately $aa:ab:bc:cd:dd = 2:1:2:1:12$. Genital tumescences surround setae ab on segment xvi also often on ix, $xvii$, $xxii–xxv$, xxx (Fig. 24).

Anterior septa, 5/6–9/10 (10/11), only feebly thickened. Seminal vesicles three pairs in segments ix, xi and xii but the anterior pair may be rudimentary or absent.

Capsules: Length 1.5–3.5 mm, diameter 1.5–2.9 mm. Usually opaque but occasionally transparent, pale green to greenish yellow colour; surface smooth.

Reproduction: Some populations biparental, others uniparental (?parthenogenetic); male sterility and absence of spermathecae common.

Habitat: Woodland species found under moss and loose bark on old trees and in rotting wood, common in moist litter and under stones in wet habitats, present in marshes; common in leaf mould and rich garden soils, compost, manure heaps, sewage filtration beds and under dung in grasslands. Recorded from caves.

Distribution: Holarctic: Manchuria and western Siberia westwards to the western United States (Washington) south to North Africa and Mexico. Fossil capsules have been recovered from deposits 10 000 years old in Ontario (Schwert, 1979). Introduced into northern India, Australasia, Central and South America and several oceanic islands.

British records: Widespread.

Notes:

(1) Known as bank worm, tree worm, cockspur, gilt tail, gold-tailed brandling.

(2) This is a polymorphic species with the male reproductive system variably developed causing breeding divergence and variation in the expression of secondary sexual characters, for example the tubercula pubertatis that are often used as taxonomic characters. Four morphs have been recognized: *rubidus*, *subrubicundus*, *tenuis* and *norvegicus*. The last is unknown in Britain although the others are widespread and often occur together. For example, Boyd (1956) recorded this species from 13 Hebridean islands, with the three British morphs present on ten of the islands under dung-pats and the *tenuis* morph dominant in dunes and machair.

(3) The chromosome number is variable. In Britain morph *rubidus* has 34 chromosomes, *subrubicundus* 68, *tenuis* 48 but in Italy *subrubicundus* possesses only 34 chromosomes while both *rubidus* in Greenland and *tenuis* in the eastern Alps have 102 chromosomes.

Genus EISENIA Malm, 1877

Calciferous sacs absent. Calciferous gland opening directly into the oesophagus in segment *xi*. Nephridial vesicles sausage-shaped, turning down into the parietes mesially without definite ducts. Nephridiopores inconspicuous, alternating irregularly and with asymmetry on each side of the body anywhere above setal line *b*. Pigment red.

Eisenia andrei Bouché

Eisenia foetida var. *unicolor* André, 1963:24.
Eisenia fetida andrei Bouché, 1972:381; Jaenike, 1982:6.
Eisenia unicolor Øien and Stenersen, 1984:277.

Apart from pigmentation this species is superficially indistinguishable from *Eisenia fetida* (p. 80). The two species differ visually only in *andrei* being more intensely pigmented with a uniform vinous red-brown colouration and lacking the unpigmented, whitish cream intersegmental areas characteristic of the striped *fetida*. Electrophoretic surveys however reveal a total reproductive isolation between the two species (Jaenike, 1982; Øien and Stenersen, 1984). Size ranges, segment number variations and other morphological data, not recorded.

Habitat: Known only from (low pH) cultures of *Eisenia fetida*.

Distribution: Reported sporadically from commercial cultures in Britain, France, Italy, Norway and from both laboratory and commercial cultures in the United States.

Notes:

André (1963) named worms of this species *Eisenia fetida* var. *unicolor* but varietal names proposed after 1961 are regarded as infrasubspecific and outside of nomenclature. Bouché (1972) however provided the species with a valid name, a patronym, to acknowledge the importance of André's studies.

80

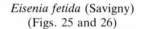

Eisenia fetida (Savigny)
(Figs. 25 and 26)

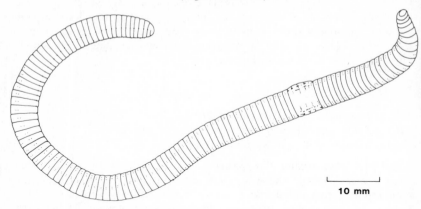

10 mm

Fig. 25. *Eisenia fetida.* Whole animal (drawn by Solene Morris).

Enterion fetidum Savigny, 1826:182.
Eisenia foetida: Michaelsen, 1900:475; Tétry, 1937:143; Gerard, 1964:26; Gates, 1972a:97; Gates, 1978b:133.
Eisenia fetida fetida: Bouché, 1972:380.

Length (35) 60–120 (130) mm, diameter (2) 3–6 mm, segment number (65) 80–120. Body cylindrical becoming trapezoidal posteriorly. Colour variable from light pink through vinous hues to purplish red or brown, confined to the equatorial region of each segment often as narrow transverse stripes on the dorsum; pigmentless yellowish white bands extending from the furrows with the ventrum often entirely pigmentless. (For totally pigmented, uniformly coloured individuals, see *Eisenia andrei.*)

Prostomium epilobous. First dorsal pore in furrow (3/4) 4/5; dorsal pores small. Spermathecal pores two pairs in furrows 9/10/11, located dorsally at least ⅓ the distance from setal line *d* to the mid-dorsal line (usually ½ to ⅔). Male pores paired on segment *xv* between setal lines *b* and *c* with a small oval tumescence confined to segment *xv*. Clitellum covering six to eight segments (*xxiv*) (*xxv*) *xxvi–xxxii* (*xxxiii*) (*xxxiv*); saddle-shaped. Tubercula pubertatis form paired narrow bands along the ventral borders of the clitellum just laterally to setal lines *bb*, usually over three segments but sometimes impinging onto adjacent segments (*xxvii*) *xxviii–xxx* (*xxxi*) (*xxxii*) (Figs. 25 and 26a).

Setae closely paired, post-clitellar formula $aa:ab:bc:cd:dd = 4:1:4:1:16$. Genital tumescences often around either or both the ventral and dorsal (lateral) setal pairs on some of segments *ix–xii* also occasionally on

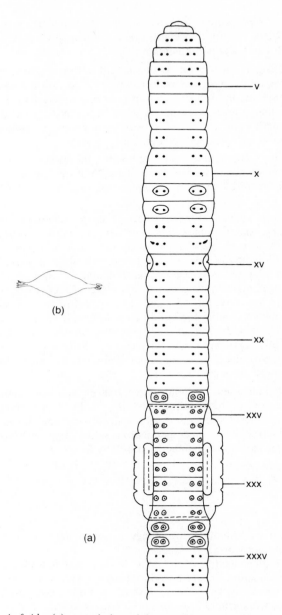

Fig. 26. *Eisenia fetida.* (*a*) ventral view of the anterior region and (*b*) egg capsule.

segments *xvii–xxiii*; present around setae *ab* in the clitellar region (Fig. 26a). Septa 6/7/8/9 slightly thickened, other anterior septa delicate. Seminal vesicles with four pairs in segments *ix–xii*.

Capsules: Length 2.4–5.2 mm, diameter 2.3–4.4 mm; spherical to sickle-shaped. Opaque, greenish yellow darkening with age; surface smooth. Eight to twenty embryos in each capsule but only one to five hatchlings emerge (lowest numbers develop from capsules deposited during the winter); hatchling length up to 14 mm but shorter when several hatchlings complete development in a single capsule (Fig. 26b).

Reproduction: Biparental, in isolation facultatively self-fertilizing (parthenogenesis not proven) (Hartenstein, Neuhauser and Easton, 1980). Spermatophores disc-like, often present on segments *xxi–xxiii*. Chromosome number 22.

Habitat: Under damp rotting vegetation: in woodland in wet decaying leaf litter and under sodden logs spreading to most low pH situations (pH 4.3–7.5) such as rich organic soils in cultivation; commonly under compost, seldom absent from standing manure heaps and sewage filter beds where it can tolerate low concentrations of ammonia. Reported from caves. Often found at night moving over the surface of land where compost or manure have been recently spread. The only British earthworm to be reported regularly from inside buildings: emerging from between flagstones and cracked concrete floors in old dilapidated premises, living in accumulated dirt and grease in corners and crevices in ill-kept accommodation, occurring sporadically in the traps of drains and lavatory pans where cracked or broken sewer pipes afford access.

Distribution: Palaearctic, seldom above 1000 m, now widespread in other temperate regions of the world, usually associated with cultivation especially around major cities. Occurs only sporadically in the tropics presumably from repeated re-introductions since populations seldom approach the density of those of other earthworm families and usually fail.

British records: Widespread.

Notes:

(1) Known as brandling, brindling, bramlin, bramble worm, manure worm and tiger worm (N. America).

(2) The original spelling of the name *fetida* is now followed replacing the invalid emendation *foetida* introduced many years ago by Dugès (1837).

(3) The species is noted for exuding an unpleasant smelling (fetid), yellowish coelomic fluid from the dorsal pores when alarmed. Although the species is distasteful to some fish, generally its use as a bait is favoured by anglers.

(4) The species is widely reared on earthworm farms on both sides of

the Atlantic. In recent years it has been employed to break down slurried pig manure when large populations result. The earthworms can be extracted and fed to the pigs as a protein supplement to their diet so enhancing the growth rates, i.e. raising pork production.

Eisenia hortensis (Michaelsen)
(Fig. 27)

Allolobophora subrubicunda hortensis Michaelsen, 1890 : 15.
Eisenia veneta hortensis : Michaelsen, 1900 : 477.
Dendrobaena veneta hortensis : Gerard, 1964 : 39.
Eisenia hortensis : Gates 1968a : 1; Gates, 1972a : 103.
Allolobophora hibernica Friend, 1892 : 402.
Eisenia veneta hibernica : Michaelsen, 1900 : 477.
Dendrobaena veneta hibernica : Gerard, 1964 : 38.
Eisenia hibernica : Gates, 1975b : 2.
Allolobophora veneta tepidaria Friend, 1904 : 161.
Eisenia veneta tepidaria : Cernosvitov, 1942 : 239.
Allolobophora veneta dendroidea Friend, 1909 : 243.
Eisenia veneta dendroidea : Cernosvitov, 1942 : 240.
Dendrobaena veneta hibernica dendroidea : Gerard, 1964 : 39.
Allolobophora (Eisenia) veneta robusta Friend, 1909 : 246.
Eisenia veneta robusta : Cernosvitov, 1942 : 239,

Length 20–50 mm, diameter 1.5–5 mm, segment number 42–130. Body cylindrical with the posterior region somewhat rhomboid and depressed. Colour variable, rosy to reddish purple above extending ventrally over the first fifteen segments and often in the caudal region, otherwise whitish yellow below.

Prostomium epi- to tanylobous. First dorsal pore in furrow 5/6. Spermathecal pores paired in furrows 9/10/11, located near the mid-dorsal line. Male pores paired on segment *xv* with small tumescences confined by the furrows 14/15 and 15/16. Clitellum extends over segments (*xxvi*) *xxvii–xxxiii*, saddle-shaped reaching down nearly to setal line *b*. Tubercula pubertatis may form translucent elliptical bands or ridges over segments *xxx, xxxi* and sometimes impinging into *xxix* and *xxxii*, usually seen as two pairs of pads; furrow 30/31 not obliterated (Fig. 27).

Setae widely paired, post-clitellar formula $aa : ab : bc : cd : dd = 1.5 : 1 : 1.5 : 1 : 3$. Genital tumescences surround setae *ab* on segments (*ix*), (*x*), *xi*, *xii* and in the clitellar region; but often lacking (Fig. 27).

Septa 13/14/15 strongly muscular. Seminal vesicles paired usually in four segments *ix–xii* but either or both of the anterior pairs, i.e. in segments *ix* and/or *x*, may be rudimentary or fail to develop.

Capsules: Not recorded.

Reproduction: Biparental. Chromosome number 36.

Habitat: Decaying forest litter: now widespread in organic rich soils of greenhouses, gardens and pastures; encountered near septic tank and wet soils recently treated with sewage.

Distribution: Caucasus, Turkey, Greece, Albania, Italy, Switzerland, Germany and Portugal. Introduced into India (Darjiling), South Africa (Port

85

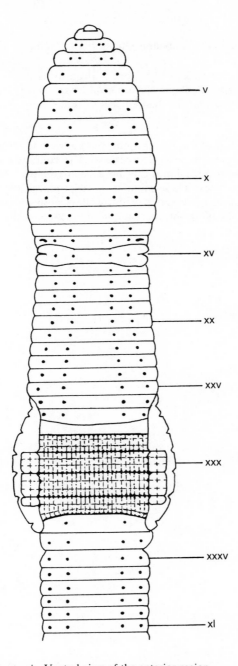

Fig. 27. Eisenia hortensis. Ventral view of the anterior region.

Elizabeth), Argentina, Chile and United States (Oregon, California, Ohio, Virginia).

British records: Introduced (?): Dorset (Bradstock), Oxfordshire (Botanic Gardens, Oxford; Blenheim Palace Gardens), Surrey (Kew Gardens), Worcestershire (Malvern), Channel Islands (Guernsey) and Eire.

Notes:

The morphology of this worm is not well known and the species has been described as new on several occasions. The confusion seemingly stems from the diverse techniques that have been employed to relax, kill and preserve specimens. These methods have produced differing degrees of contraction of the muscles of the body wall so causing variations not only in the shape of the body but, more important taxonomically, also in the setal ratios.

Eisenia veneta (Rosa)
(Fig. 28)

Allolobophora veneta Rosa, 1886:674.
Eisenia veneta: Michaelsen, 1900:477.
Dendrobaena veneta typica: Gerard, 1964:38.
Dendrobaena (Dendrobaena) veneta veneta: Bouché, 1972:398.
Eisenia veneta zebra Michaelsen, 1902:39.
Dendrobaena veneta zebra: Gerard, 1964:39.
Eisenia zebra: Gates, 1969:453.

Length 50–155 mm, diameter 4–8 mm, segment number 86–255.

Body cylindrical, posterior region often tending to become rectangular in transverse section, possibly depressed. Colour, a conspicuous reddish purple mid-dorsal stripe with intrasegmental bands mainly incomplete ventrally except possibly for a few anterior segments, intersegmental furrows and most of the ventral suface unpigmented flesh colour to whitish yellow; the pigmentation of the dorsum in the anterior region is often dense and may spread into the furrows (*see* p. 44).

Prostomium variable from proepilobous through epilobous to tanylobous. First dorsal pore in furrow 5/6. Spermathecal pores paired in furrows 9/10/11 located near the mid-dorsal line. Male pores paired with large tumescences confined to segment *xv*. Clitellum over segments (*xxvi*) *xxvii–xxxii* (*xxxiii*), saddle-shaped extending to below setal line *c*. Tubercula pubertatis extend at least over segments *xxx, xxxi* and often into *xxix* and /or *xxxii*, usually ridge-like but the furrows are seldom completely obliterated; occasionally papillate and nearly circular on segments *xxx* and *xxxi* only (Fig. 28a).

Setae widely paired, post-clitellar formula $aa:ab:bc:cd:dd = 1.5:1:1.5:1:3$. Genital tumescences usually surround setae *ab* in the clitellar region, at least on segments *xxx* and *xxxi* (Fig. 28a).

Most of the anterior septa thickened: 5/6–12/13 slightly muscular, 13/14/15 strongly muscular. Seminal vesicles paired in four segments, *ix, x, xi, xii*.

Capsules: Length 3.2–5.1 mm, diameter 3.0–3.6 mm. Colour, light lemon-yellow darkening to brown with age; one pole is markedly thicker than the other. At a temperature of 18°C, worms produced three capsules a week and embryonic development was completed in six weeks (Fig. 28b).

Reproduction: Biparental. Spermatophores may be present ventrally especially in the regions of segments *xxvii–xxix*. Chromosome number 36.

Habitat: Under decaying leaves, commonly in organic rich soils; recorded from compost, manure and sewage beds.

Distribution: Caucasus westwards through the Levant to Italy (described from Venice) onto Spain. Recently recorded in California (San Francisco).

British records: Introduced: Surrey (Kew Gardens, Mitcham, Raynes Park), Lancashire (Lancaster), Staffordshire (Keele), Cumbria, Worcestershire, North Wales (Borth) and South Wales (Rhondda Valley) also Eire (Dublin).

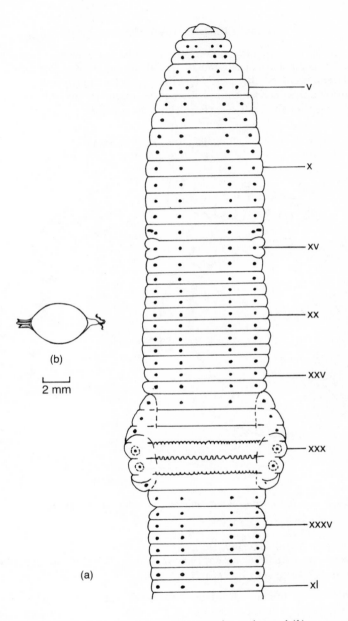

(b)

2 mm

(a)

V

X

XV

XX

XXV

XXX

XXXV

Xl

Fig. 28. *Eisenia veneta*. (*a*) ventral view of the anterior region and (*b*) egg capsule.

Genus EISENIELLA Michaelsen, 1900

Calciferous sacs opening posteriorly into the oesophagus in segment x ventrally just in front of septum 10/11. Calciferous lamellae continued along the lateral walls of the sacs. Nephridial vesicles shortly sausage-shaped. Nephridiopores inconspicuous, alternating irregularly and with asymmetry on each side of the body anywhere above setal line b.

Eiseniella tetraedra (Savigny)
(Figs. 29 and 30)

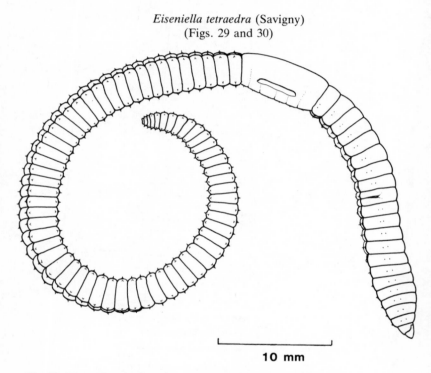

10 mm

Fig. 29. *Eiseniella tetraedra*. Whole animal (drawn by Mandy Holloway).

Enterion tetraedrum Savigny, 1826:183.
Eiseniella tetraedra: Michaelsen, 1900:471; Tétry, 1937:142; Gerard, 1964:42; Bouché, 1972:215; Gates, 1977b:71.

Length (20)30–65 mm, diameter 1.5–4.0 mm, segment number (60)70–90(160). Body cylindrical anteriorly, post-clitellar region quadrangular in transverse section with a pair of setae at each of the four corners, tapering caudally. Colour dark brownish green often with reddish brown or golden yellow hues.

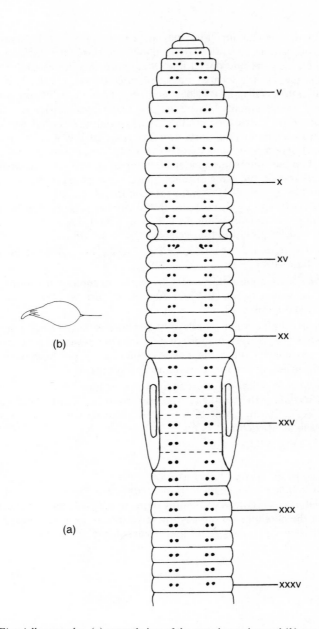

Fig. 30. *Eiseniella tetraedra.* (*a*) ventral view of the anterior region and (*b*) egg capsule.

Prostomium epilobous. First dorsal pore in furrow 4/5. Spermathecal pores, two pairs in furrows 9/10/11 about two-thirds the distance between setal line *d* and the mid-dorsal line. Male pores paired usually on segment *xiii*, infrequently *xv*, located on small tumescences confined to a single segment, i.e. usually on *xiii*, between setal lines *bc*. Clitellum commonly extending over segments (*xxii*) *xxiii–xxvi* (*xxvii*); saddle-shaped. Tubercula pubertatis form narrow longitudinal bands along the ventral border of the clitellum in segments (*xxii* part) *xxiii–xxv* (Figs 29 and 30a).

Setae closely paired, immediate post-clitellar formula $aa:ab:bc:cd:dd = 3:1:3:1:6$ but due to the hinder body tapering while the members of the setal pairs remain the same distance apart, more caudally the setal formula becomes $2.5:1:2.5:1:4$. Genital tumescences often surround setae *ab* on segments (*viii*) (*ix*) *x* (xi) (*xii*) also in the clitellar region (Figs 29 and 30a).

Anterior septa mainly delicate although 7/8–11/12 are feebly muscular. Seminal vesicles paired in four segments *ix, x, xi, xii*.

Capsules: Length 1.2–2.6 mm, diameter 1.1–2.3 mm; ovoid. Opaque, pale yellow often with a green hue (Fig. 30b).

Reproduction: Uniparental seemingly parthenogenetic but spermatophores present occasionally on the ventrum near furrows 19/20 and 20/21. Chromosome number 72.

Habitat: In running water, ponds or wells under stones or among the roots of water plants, or, in wet situations in the banks of streams and other soils near water; also in caves. Found in a wide range of soil types from peaty organic material, including sewage, to sand and gravel (pH 4.6–8.5).

Distribution: Western Palaearctic now introduced into other temperate regions including the northern Nearctic, southern South America, South Africa, Australia and New Zealand. Sporadically with water plants elsewhere such as Mexico and India.

British records: Widespread.

Notes:

(1) Known as squared-tailed worm.

(2) Morphologically highly variable with a few variants present in most populations. Variations commonly occur in the position of the male pores and of the clitellum. In the past these variations were recognized taxonomically but the names are no longer considered to be valid.

Genus HELODRILUS Hoffmeister, 1845

Calciferous sacs absent. Calciferous gland opens directly into the oesophagus in segment x. Calciferous lamellae extend midway through segment x. Nephridial vesicles absent. Nephridiopores obvious in a single row along each side of the body. Pigment, if present, *not* red.

94

Helodrilus oculatus Hoffmeister
(Fig. 31)

Helodrilus oculatus Hoffmeister, 1845:39; Michaelsen, 1900:497; Gerard, 1964:45; Bouché, 1972:431.

Length 35–80 mm, diameter 1–2 mm, segment number 90–150. Body cylindrical. Colour flesh occasionally with scattered black markings otherwise unpigmented. Prostomium epilobous. First dorsal pore in furrow 4/5. Spermathecal pores, two pairs located in furrows 9/10/11 immediately below setal line *c*. Male pores paired on segment *xv* in setal line *b* with large tumescences extending up to between furrows 13/14–16/17. Clitellum long, extending from segment (*xxi*) *xxii–xxxii*; saddle-shaped. Tubercula pubertatis form an ovoid, longitudinal ridge along ventral border of the clitellum in segments *xxix* and *xxx* (Fig. 31).

Setae closely paired, post-clitellar formula *aa* : *ab* : *bc* : *cd* : *dd* = 7 : 1.2 : 5 : 1 : 15. Genital tumescences surround setae *ab* on segments (*x*) *xi* (*xii*) (Fig. 31).

Septa 6/7/8/9 strongly muscular, septa 5/6 and 9/10 less so. Seminal vesicles, two pairs in segments *xi* and *xii*.

Capsules: Not recorded.

Reproduction: No details. Chromosome number 32.

Habitat: In running water, ponds and wells in the substratum, or, in wet situations in clay and muds of river banks, ditches and ponds; not acid tolerant (pH 7.0–7.6).

Distribution: France, Belgium, Netherlands, Germany, Switzerland, Italy, Austria, Czechoslovakia, Poland and USSR.

British records: Southern England (River Thames, Hastings, St. Albans, Kew and Malvern) and Eire (Dublin and Lough Mask).

Notes:

Populations often consist almost entirely of juveniles which are characterized by the terminal setae not being black. Found in layers of partially decomposed vegetation 3–5 m deep in a Roman ditch at Verulamium (St. Albans). This record has led to speculation that the species may have been endemic in England in pre-historic times if not introduced by the Romans during the 1st century A.D. (Dobson and Satchell, 1956).

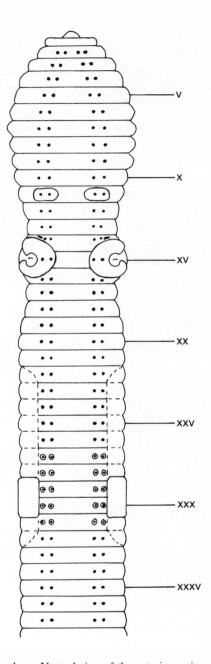

Fig. 31. *Helodrilus oculatus*. Ventral view of the anterior region.

Genus LUMBRICUS Linnaeus, 1758

Calciferous sacs opening posteriorly into the oesophagus of segment x ventrally and just in front of septum 10/11. Calciferous lamellae continued along the lateral walls of the sacs. Nephridial vesicles J-shaped. Nephridiopores obvious, alternating irregularly and with asymmetry on each side of the body above setal line b. Prostomium tanylobous. Pigment red.

Lumbricus castaneus (Savigny)
(Fig. 32)

Enterion castaneum Savigny, 1826:180.
Lumbricus castaneus: Michaelsen, 1900:510; Tétry, 1937:151; Gerard, 1964:46; Bouché, 1972:362; Gates, 1978a:94.

Length 30–45(70) mm, diameter 2–4mm, segment number (72) 85–90(100). Body cylindrical, posterior region slightly depressed. Colour red-brown (chestnut) to violet brown above, strongly iridescent; paler, brownish yellow below; pigmented.

Prostomium tanylobous. First dorsal pore in furrow 6/7. Spermathecal pores paired in furrows 9/10/11 almost in setal line c. Male pores paired on segment xv between setal lines bc, inconspicuous but the sourrounding area may be raised slightly to form a low tumescence. Clitellum extends over segments ($xxvii$) $xxviii–xxxiii$ ($xxxiv$); saddle-shaped. Tubercula pubertatis form narrow bands on segments $xxix–xxxii$ lying along the ventral margins of the clitellum above setal line b (Fig. 32).

Setae closely paired, post-clitellar formula $aa:ab:bc:cd:dd = 5:1.2:5:1:20$. Genital tumescences surround setae ab usually only on segment x, occasionally ix and xi (Fig. 32).

Anterior septa not noticeably muscular. Seminal vesicles, three pairs in segments ix, xi, xii; those in xii often enlarged and may extend to segment xv.

Capsules: Length 1.9–3.0 mm, diameter 1.7–2.6mm; ovoid. Opaque, pale olive brown; surface matt.

Reproduction: Obligatory biparental; copulation mainly in the soil or under a covering of leaves or stones. Chromosome number 36.

Habitat: Decaying leaves, manure and faeces, soils mostly with a high organic content (pH 3.9–8.4); under logs and stones in woodland, marshes, river banks, caves, gardens, pasture and arable land.

Distribution: Palaearctic region (excluding the Iberian peninsula) and eastern North America, spreading throughout the Nearctic. Occasionally introduced elsewhere, e.g. New Zealand, St. Helena.

British records: Widespread.

Notes:
   Known as chestnut worm, marsh worm or purple worm but see *L. rubellus* (p. 104).

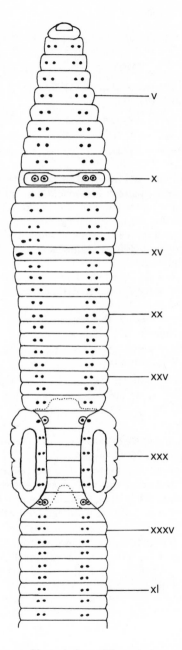

Fig. 32. *Lumbricus castaneus*. Ventral view of the anterior region.

Lumbricus eiseni Levinsen
(Fig. 33)

Lumbricus eiseni Levinsen, 1884:241; Gates, 1968b:1; Gates, 1978a:115.
Helodrilus (Bimastos) eiseni: Michaelsen, 1900:503.
Bimastos eiseni: Gerard, 1964:33.
Eisenia eiseni: Bouché, 1972:385.

Length 30–64 mm, diameter 2–5 mm, segment number (70)99–115.
Body cylindrical. Colour purplish to brownish red or slate, more yellowish
below; pigmented. Prostomium tanylobous. First dorsal pore in furrow 5/6. Spermathecal
pores absent. Male pores paired on conspicuous tumescences confined to
segment *xv*, one-third of the distance from seta *b* to seta *c*. Clitellum extends
over segments *xxiv–xxxii* (*xxxii*) reaching down to within setal lines *aa*;
saddle-shaped, infrequently nearly annular when the ventral borders of the
clitellum in some of the mid-clitellar segments meet mid-ventrally. Tubercula
pubertatis absent (Fig. 33a).

Setae closely paired, post-clitellar formula $aa:ab:bc:cd:dd =$
$5:1.2:5:1:10$. Genital tumescences sometimes present around setae *ab* on
segments *xvi, xvii, xxv* (Fig. 33a).

Septa 6/7/8/9 only slightly thickened. Seminal vesicles, two pairs,
rudimentary in segments *xi, xii*.

Capsules: Length 2.8–4.8 mm, diameter 2.2–3.5 mm; ovoid, Translucent
golden brown; surface smooth (Fig. 33b).

Reproduction: Details unknown, probably parthenogenetic (spermatozoa
scarce in the male ducts, or absent) but copulation occurs on occasions
(spermatophores, lacking spermatozoa, sometimes present in the clitellar
region). Chromosome number 32.

Habitat: Under moss and decaying leaves, often the dominant earthworm in
moorland, bog soils and by streams; pH 3.6–7.6.

Distribution: Widespread in western Europe westwards from Poland,
Czechoslovakia and Bulgaria; introduced into Madeira, Azores, Canary
Islands, St. Helena, United States (Tennessee and Alaska), South Africa,
western Himalayas (Naini Tal), New Zealand (North Island and Stewart
Island).

British records: Widespread in wet acid moorlands including Scottish islands,
Isle of Man, Channel Islands (Herm); recorded from Eire (Dublin).

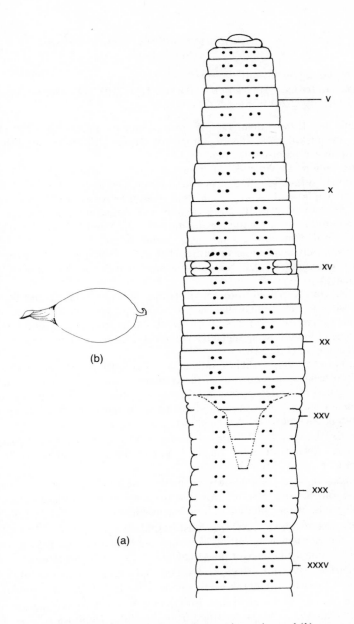

Fig. 33. *Lumbricus eiseni.* (*a*) ventral view of the anterior region and (*b*) egg capsule.

Lumbricus festivus (Savigny)
(Fig. 34)

Enterion festivum Savigny, 1826:180.
Lumbricus festivus: Michaelsen, 1900:512; Tétry, 1937:153; Gerard, 1964:46; Bouché, 1972:361; Gates, 1978a:98.

Length 48–110mm, diameter 3.5–6mm, segment number 100–120 (143). Body cylindrical, posterior region slightly depressed. Colour purplish red-brown above, paler below; pigmented.

Prostomium tanylobous. First dorsal pore in furrow 5/6 (6/7), fully functional in furrow 7/8. Spermathecal pores, two pairs in furrows 9/10/11 located within setal lines *cd*. Male pores paired on segment *xv* between setal lines *bc* with moderately sized tumescences occasionally confined to the segment but more often obliterating furrows 14/15 and 15/16 and spreading to ⅔xiv–½xvi. Clitellum extends over segments (⅓xxxiii) *xxxiv–xl* reaching down ventrally nearly to setal line *b*. Tubercula pubertatis in the form of a broad longitudinal ridge along the ventral margin of the clitellum over segments *xxxv–xxxviii* (Fig. 34).

Setae closely paired with the distances between setae *a* and setae *b* increasing in the pre-clitellar and caudal regions; post-clitellar formula $aa:ab:bc:cd:dd = 5:1.2:4:1:18$. Genital tumescences surround setae *ab* on many of the following segments *viii–xiv*, *xviii*, *xxv–xxvii* in addition to the clitellar region (Fig. 34).

Septa 6/7/8/9 only slightly muscular, septa 9/10/11 delicate and largely adherent causing a reduction in the coelomic cavity of segment *x* and the three pairs of seminal vesicles seeming to occur in adjacent segments. Seminal vesicles, three pairs in segments *ix, xi, xii* with the posterior pair extending back perhaps to segment *xv*.

Capsules: Length 2.6–4.5mm, diameter 2.4–3.5mm; spherical. Opaque, medium brown with green tinge, darker at the poles; surface matt and uniform, without fibrous layers.

Reproduction: Details unknown, probably obligatory biparental; copulation in the soil. Spermatophores reported from the ventral surface before the anterior end of the clitellum. Chromosome number 36.

Habitat: Although recorded from pastures this worm occurs mainly in damp, often acid soils such as rotting vegetation and manure; also present under logs and stones and in river banks (pH 4.5–8.2). Never numerous.

Distribution: Western Europe: Sweden, Denmark, Germany, Belgium, northern France; Canada (New Brunswick, Quebec, British Colombia).

British records: Widespread from Eire to the Channel Islands (Guernsey) but rare in Scotland although recorded from the Outer Hebrides.
Notes:
Known as ruddy worm.

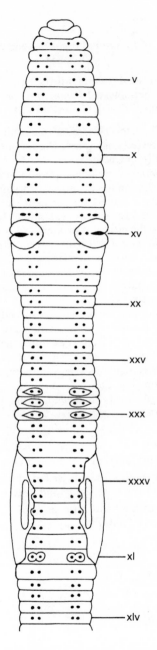

Fig. 34. *Lumbricus festivus*. Ventral view of the anterior region.

Lumbricus friendi Cognetti
(Fig. 35)

Lumbricus papillosus Friend, 1893:1; Michaelsen, 1900:512.
Lumbricus friendi Cognetti, 1904:10 [*nom. nov.* pro *Lumbricus papillosus*
Friend, 1893 (*non* Müller, 1776)]; Gerard, 1964:47; Bouché, 1972:356.

Length 45–120mm, diameter 4–8mm, segment number 70–130.
Body cylindrical, depressed posteriorly. Colour purplish red or brownish red
dorsally, paler ventrally; pigmented.

Prostomium tanylobous. First dorsal pore in furrow 6/7 or close behind,
often difficult to see. Spermathecal pores two pairs in furrows 9/10/11 by
setal line *d*. Male pores paired on segment *xv* just below setal line *c*,
moderate sized tumescence usually extending beyond the furrows and
impinging slightly onto the adjacent segments *xiv* and *xvi*. Clitellum covering
segments (½*xxxii*) *xxxiii–xxxvii* (½*xxxviii*) reaching down ventrally to setal line
c. Tubercula pubertatis form a slender ridge over segments *xxxiv–xxxvi*
(xxxvii) between setal lines *bc* below the border of the clitellum, commonly
saucer-like/papillate in only segments *xxxiv* and *xxxvi* perhaps with a feeble
linking ridge in segment *xxxv*.

Setae closely paired but more widely spaced (and stouter) towards
the anterior and caudal regions, immediate post-clitellar formula
aa:*ab*:*bc*:*cd*:*dd* = 7:1.5:6:1:22. Genital tumescences often surround setae
ab on segments *ix, x, xi* also the individual raised areas tend to merge to form
a continuous band across segments *xxix–xl* although the setae may be absent
from the clitellar region (Fig. 35).

Anterior septa not obviously thickened. Seminal vesicles, three pairs in
segments *ix, xi, xii* with the posterior pair usually extending back perhaps to
segment *xv*.

Capsules: Not recorded.

Reproduction: Obligatory biparental. Chromosome number 36.

Habitat: Occurs mainly under forest litter but known from pastures and wet
garden soils; recorded from both sandy and calcareous soils (pH 4.0–8.0).

Distribution: Austria, Switzerland, France, Spain.

British records: Channel Islands (Jersey), Wales (Bangor), Eire (Dublin and
Johnstown); rare.

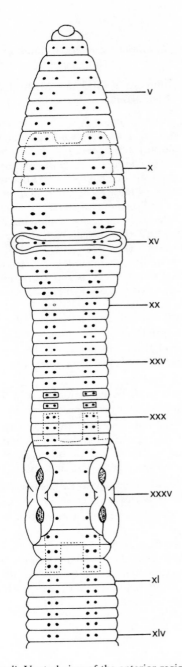

Fig. 35. *Lumbricus friendi*. Ventral view of the anterior region.

104

Lumbricus rubellus Hoffmeister
(Fig. 36)

Lumbricus rubellus Hoffmeister, 1843:187; Michaelsen, 1900:509; Gerard, 1964:47; Bouché, 1972:362; Gates, 1978a:100.

Length (25) 60–130(140)mm, diameter 3–4mm, segment number (70) 101–119 (126). Body cylindrical, posterior region commonly slightly depressed. Colour brownish to purplish red above, pale yellow below; pigmented.

Prostomium tanylobous. First dorsal pore in furrow (6/7) 7/8 (8/9). Spermathecal pores, two pairs in furrows 9/10/11 opening in setal line *c*. Male pores paired on segment *xv* midway between setal lines *bc*, inconspicuous. Clitellum spreading over segments (½*xxvi*) *xxvii–xxxii* with the ventral borders midway between setal lines *bc*. Tubercula pubertatis form broad bands along the ventral borders of the clitellum almost touching setal line *b* in segments (⅔*xxvii*) *xxviii–xxxi* (Fig. 36a).

Setae closely paired, post-clitellar formula $aa:ab:bc:cd:dd = 6:1.2:6:1:20$. Genital tumescences usually surround setae *ab* on some or all of segments *x, xi, xii, xxii* and on segments at both ends of the clitellum (Fig. 36a).

Septa 7/8/9 slightly thickened. Seminal vesicles, three pairs in segments *ix, xi, xii* with the posterior pair often extending into segment *xiii*.

Capsules: Length 1.6–4.1mm, diameter 1.6–3.3mm; spherical. Opaque, dirty olive-brown colour; surface matt, covered by fibrous material (Fig. 36b).

Reproduction : Obligatory biparental; copulation in the soil or in the litter layer, mucous tube lacking. Chromosome number 36.

Habitat: Recorded from a wide range of habitats but usually moist with a high organic content: in decaying leaves, under stones and moss, in river banks and ditches, in parks, gardens and pastures; recorded from soils with pH 3.5–8.4. Commonly aggregates under dung pats in pastures.

Distribution: Holarctic, introduced into peninsular India (also the Nicobar Islands), South Africa, New Zealand and several temperate oceanic islands.

British records: Widely distributed, often numerous.

Notes:

(1) Known as red worm or redhead.

(2) This species is often reared for fish bait and most anglers confuse it with the smaller *Lumbricus castaneus* (p. 96) so that the following vernacular names could apply to both species: black-headed red worm, segg worm, trout worm and button worm (Friend, 1924).

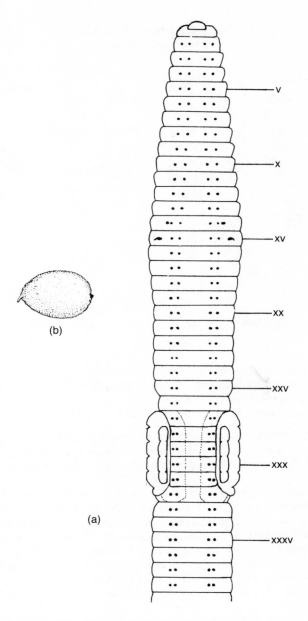

V

X

XV

XX

XXV

XXX

XXXV

(a)

(b)

Fig. 36. *Lumbricus rubellus*. (*a*) ventral view of the anterior region and (*b*) egg capsule.

Lumbricus terrestris Linnaeus
(Figs. 1, 37 and 38)

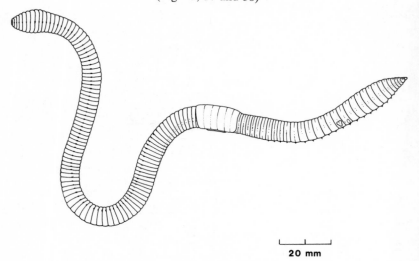

20 mm

Fig. 37. *Lumbricus Terrestris*. Whole animal (drawn by Mandy Holloway).

Lumbricus terrestris Linnaeus, 1758:647; Michaelsen, 1900:511; Gerard, 1964:48; Sims, 1973:27; Bouché, 1976:86; Gates, 1978a:82.
Enterion herculeum Savigny, 1826:180.
Lumbricus herculeus: Tétry, 1937:151; Bouché, 1972:352.

Length 90–350mm, diameter 6–10mm, segment number (120) 140–155 (160). Body cylindrical, posterior region depressed and strongly paddle-shaped. Colour brownish to purplish red above, yellow-orange below; pigmented.

Prostomium tanylobous. First dorsal pore in furrow (7/8) 8/9. Spermathecal pores, two pairs in furrows 9/10/11 midway between setal lines *cd*. Male pores paired on segment *xv* in setal line *b* with prominent tumescences commonly impinging onto the adjacent segments but never obliterating the furrows; tumescences usually regress after breeding. Clitellum extends over segments *xxxii–xxxvii* (*xxxviii*), saddle-shaped reaching down to setal line *b*. Tubercula pubertatis in the form of a longitudinal ridge along the ventral borders of the clitellum on segments (½*xxxii*) *xxxiii–xxxvi* (½*xxxvii*) (Figs. 1 and 38a).

Setae closely paired except in the anterior and flattened caudal regions where more distant and stouter, immediate post-clitellar formula *aa* : *ab* : *bc* : *cd* : *dd* = 6 : 1.3 : 5 : 1 : 22. Genital tumescences surround setae *ab*

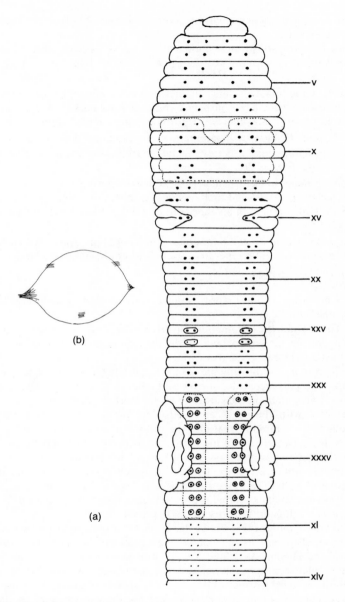

Fig. 38. *Lumbricus terrestris*. (*a*) ventral view of the anterior region and (*b*) egg capsule.

on some or all of segments *viii–xiv*, *xxiv* and in the vicinity of the clitellum (Figs. 1 and 38a).

Septa 6/7/8/9/10 strongly muscular. Seminal vesicles, three pairs in segments *ix*, *xi*, *xii* with the posterior pair commonly filling most of segment *xiii*.

Capsules: Length 4.4–7.3 mm, diameter 3.9–5.7 mm; spherical. Opaque, medium brown with a greenish hue, base of tufts darker; fibrous surface composed of several layers (Fig. 38b). Hatchling length 25 mm.

Reproduction: Obligatory biparental; copulation takes place on the surface of the soil. Spermatophores rare, found ventrally over segments *xxiv–xxvii*. Chromosome number 36.

Habitat: In many undisturbed, terrestrial habitats, most numerous in grass-lands (including lawns) and orchards, less common in woodland, arable soil and river banks. Found in alkaline soils of pH 6.2–10.0; especially abundant in clay.

Distribution: Holarctic and temperate regions of South America, Australia, New Zealand, several temperate oceanic and other southern islands.

British records: Widespread.

Notes:

(1) Known as lob, dew worm, squirrel tail, twachel or night crawler (in N. America).

(2) Though not the commonest British earthworm, it is usually exposed when digging in garden beds when the adults are recognizable as the stoutest and largest red earthworm.

(3) Nocturnal, it is the only species that regularly forages for plant material around the entrance to its burrow and emerges, especially on mild moist nights, to copulate on the surface. On these occasions the posterior region is swollen with the setae erect gripping the mouth of the burrow in readiness for a rapid retreat into the soil if danger should threaten.

(4) A distinctive feature of the burrow is the presence around the entrance of leaf stalks and twigs left projecting through small casts; such burrows are commonly found in lawns, borders, between paving stones and at the bottoms of walls. The burrow is constructed vertically to a depth of 1–3 m; a terminal chamber, sometimes lined with layers of pea-sized stones, provides a refuge in very dry or cold periods.

(5) In school biology text-books this species is usually selected for detailed study and dissection as an example of a typical earthworm and representa-tive of the phylum Annelida. Yet the morphology and physiology of the Lumbricidae are atypical not only of the Annelida but also of other families of earthworms while the specialized modes of feeding and reproduction of *Lumbricus terrestris* are not representative of the family Lumbricidae.

109

Genus MURCHIEONA Gates, 1978

Calciferous sacs with two chambers opening vertically through a U-shaped orifice into the oesophagus anterodorsally in segment *x*. Calciferous gland not constricted intersegmentally. Nephridial vesicles present. Nephridiopores obvious, in a single rank along each side of the body. Pigment absent. Prostomium epilobous.

Murchieona minuscula (Rosa)
(Fig. 39)

Allolobophora minuscula Rosa, 1906:38; Gates, 1975c:7; Zicsi, 1981:176.
Allolobophora (Bimastos) icenorum Pickford, 1926:96.
Bimastos icenorum: Gerard, 1964:34.
Allolobophora minima Muldal, 1952:463.
Bimastos muldali Omodeo, 1956:179 [*nom. nov.* pro *Allolobophora minima* Muldal, 1952 (*non* Rosa, 1884)]; Gerard, 1964:34.
Allolobophora muldali: Murchie, 1959:329; Bouché, 1972:452.
Murchieona muldali: Gates, 1978a:114.

Length (20)30–50(60) mm, diameter 1.2–2.0 mm, segment number 84–106. Body cylindrical. Colour greyish pink to red; unpigmented.

Prostomium epilobous. First dorsal pore in furrow 11/12 or 12/13, small and indistinct. Spermathecal pores paired in furrows 9/10/11 opening near setal line *d*. Male pores paired on segment *xv* between setal lines *bc* with large tumescences spreading over segments ½*xiv*–½*xvi*. Clitellum occurs on segments (*xxvi*) *xxvii–xxxiii* (*xxxiv*); saddle-shaped, the ventral borders are nearly in setal line *b*. Tubercula pubertatis frequently absent, otherwise they form a pair of barely discernible bands along the ventral edges of the clitellum in segments *xxix–xxxi* deeply incised by furrows 28/29–31/32 that may deepen above setal line *b* to form four pairs of pit-like depressions regardless of the presence or absence of the tubercula pubertatis (Fig. 39).

Setae closely paired, post-clitellar formula *aa* : *ab* : *bc* : *cd* : *dd* = 8 : 1 : 5 : 1 : 22. Genital tumescences not clearly defined, possibly surrounding setae *ab* on segments in the region of *ix–xi* and *xxvii–xxxiii* (Fig. 39).

Septa 5/6/7/8/9 slightly thickened. Seminal vesicles often absent, otherwise two pairs in segments *xi*, *xii*.

Capsules: Size and appearance not recorded. Never more than one developing embryo in each capsule.

Reproduction: Variable: some populations obligatory biparental, copulation observed and spermatophores collected; other populations seemingly parthenogenetic.

Habitat: Rare, occurring mainly in heavy soils with a high moisture content, under rotting sedge and other decaying vegetation, fallen leaves especially in woodland.

Distribution: Locally in Italy, France, Spain and the United States (Michigan and Tennessee)

British records: Rare: Cambridgeshire (Wicken); Berkshire (Whytham Wood); County Durham; Hertfordshire (Bayfordbury); Nottingham; Surrey (Kew).

Notes:

(1) A poorly known species usually difficult to identify due to the external characters seldom being well developed. It was first reported in Britain on six parthenogenetic worms from Cambridge (Pickford, 1926). Twenty-six years elapsed before it was recorded again when a population of sexually reproducing individuals was recorded from Hertfordshire (Muldal, 1952). Sexually reproducing worms have since been found in Berkshire and individuals have been discovered lying unrecognized in old collections. In France sexually reproducing worms are widespread although never numerous, only five non-sexual (?parthenogenetic) individuals have been reported (as *Allolobophora muldali* var. *pickfordi* Bouché, 1972).

(2) Ecology and breeding were studied in a population from Michigan (Murchie, 1955).

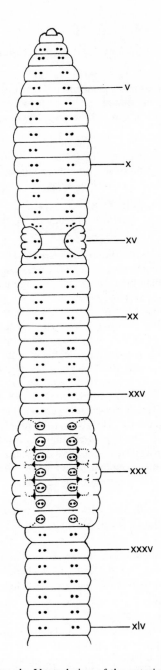

Fig. 39. *Murchieona minuscula*. Ventral view of the anterior region.

Genus OCTOLASION Örley

Calciferous sacs open vertically into the equator of the oesophagus in segment x. Calciferous lamellae continued onto the posterior walls of each sac. Nephridial vesicles ocarina-shaped. Nephridiopores obvious, seemingly in a single rank along each side of the body. Pigment, if present, *not* red. Prostomium epilobous.

Octolasion cyaneum (Savigny)
(Fig. 40)

Enterion cyaneum Savigny, 1826:181.
Octolasion cyaneum: Michaelsen, 1900:506; Tétry, 1937:150; Gerard, 1964:49; Bouché, 1972:258; Gates, 1973:31.

Length (40) 80–140 (180) mm, diameter 5–8 mm, segments number (90)150–165. Body cylindrical becoming somewhat octagonal posteriorly. Colour, blue-grey often with a lilac-blue dorsal line; unpigmented, anterior segments rosy, four or so caudal segments yellow.

Prostomium epilobous. First dorsal pore small in furrow (9/10) (10/11) 11/12 (12/13). Spermathecal pores, two pairs in furrows 9/10/11 midway between setal lines cd. Male pores paired on segment xv between setal lines bc with narrow tumescences almost entirely confined to the segment. Clitellum extends over segments $xxix–xxxiv$ ($xxxv$), saddle-shaped with the ventral margins reaching down nearly to setal line a. Tubercula pubertatis as uniformly broad bands in setal line b within the ventral borders of the clitellum on segments ($\frac{1}{2}xxix$) $xxx–xxxiii$ ($\frac{1}{2}xxxiv$) (Fig. 40a).

Setae small, inconspicuous, closely paired anteriorly becoming widely paired to distant; immediate post-clitellar formula $aa:ab:bc:cd:dd = 2.5:1.5:1.2:1:4$ (more anteriorly the setal distance ab usually approximates to bc). Genital tumescences may surround setae a or ab asymmetrically on segments $vii(ix)x$ and setae a only on segments $xvii, xviii, xix$ (xx) xxi (Fig. 40a).

Septa 7/8–12/13 only slightly thickened. Seminal vesicles, four pairs in segments ix, x, xi, xii; the two anterior pairs smaller than the two posterior pairs.

Capsules: Length 4.7–6.0 mm, diameter 3.2–4.2 mm; ovoid. Translucent, greenish yellow; surface smooth (Fig. 40b). Hatchlings usually one per capsule, rarely two; length 20 mm, anal region yellowish.

Reproduction: Obligatory parthenogenetic; copulation not recorded. Chromosome number 180, i.e. $n = (19 \times 10) - 10$.

Habitat: Locally common but never abundant, prefers moist habitats especially in limnic soils (pH 3.5–8.2), wet sands, under stones in water, in moss, on stream banks, under logs; occurs in gardens, pastures, arable land, woodland and caves.

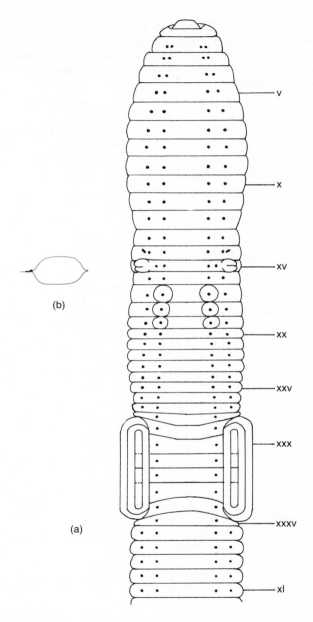

Fig. 40. *Octolasion cyaneum*. (*a*) ventral view of the anterior region and (*b*) egg capsule.

Distribution: Europe, being especially abundant in the northwest; occurs throughout most of the United States, parts of Canada, Mexico and southern South America, also introduced into northern India, Pakistan and into Australasia in addition to several temperate oceanic islands.

British records: Widespread.

Notes:

(1) Known as blue-grey worm or steel-blue worm.

(2) Frequently expelled from its burrow after heavy showers and found wandering on the surface of the ground, even in daylight.

(3) The presence of yellow granules in the coelom of the last few segments of the body is a characteristic feature.

Octolasion tyrtaeum tyrtaeum (Savigny)
(Fig. 41)

Enterion tyrtaeum Savigny, 1826:184.
Octolasion tyrtaeum: Gates, 1973:35.
Octolasion lacteum (part): Michaelsen, 1900:506; Gerard, 1964:50.
Octolasion lacteum gracile Örley, 1885:16; Bouché, 1972:257.

Length (25) 35–160 mm, diameter 2.5–6 mm, segments number (87) 100–135 (165). Body cylindrical, slightly octagonal posteriorly. Colour whitish grey to blue, rarely rosy pink or brownish; unpigmented.

Prostomium epilobous. First dorsal pore in or behind furrow 8/9, mostly between 10/11 and 12/13. Spermathecal pores paired in furrows 9/10/11, opening slightly above setal line *c*. Male pores paired on segment *xv* above setal line *b*, with large tumescences obliterating parts of furrows 14/15 and 15/16 and encroaching onto the adjacent segments to varying extents, perhaps ½*xiv*–½*xvi*. Clitellum extends over segments *xxx–xxxv*; saddle-shaped reaching down to within setal lines *ab*. Tubercula pubertatis form paired longitudinal bands within the ventral borders of the clitellum throughout its entire length, i.e. *xxx–xxxv* (Fig. 41).

Setae stout, closely paired anteriorly, becoming widely paired to distant, immediate post-clitellar formula $aa:ab:bc:cd:dd = 3.3:1.6:1.3:1.0:7.3$. Genital tumescences surround setae *ab* and often *cd* on segments (*viii*) (*ix*) *x* (*xi*) *xii* also around seta *a* on segments (*xxi*) *xxii* (*xxiii*) (Fig. 41).

Septa 6/7–14/15 muscular. Seminal vesicles, four pairs in segments *ix*, *x*, *xi*, *xii*, the two posterior pairs being larger than the two anterior pairs.

Capsules: Length 3.2–4.6 mm, diameter 2.1–3.0 mm; ovoid. Translucent, pale yellowish green; surface smooth. Only one hatchling per capsule.

Reproduction: Often reported as parthenogenetic, spermatophores unknown, but copulation within the soil has been recorded and sperm iridescence reported on the margins of the male funnels. Chromosome number 38.

Habitat: Under stones and logs, in decaying leaves, compost, peat; in soils of pH 4.3–8.1. In pasture, arable land and gardens being more abundant in moist soils of bogs, caves, stream banks and in streams among the roots of submerged vegetation.

Distribution: Records of the two subspecies (*see* 'Note' below) have been confused but *Octolasion tyrtaeum tyrtaeum* seems to occur in southern and western Europe, the Middle East and most of North America with introduced populations in South Africa, India, Australia and a few oceanic islands.

British records: Widespread, but seldom numerous.

Notes:
Two subspecies have been recognized in France (Bouché, 1972:257). The first, *Octolasion tyrtaeum tyrtaeum,* was described from Paris and occurs in

western Europe while the second *O.t.lacteum* (Örley, 1881) was described from Hungary and spreads from the Pyrenees and eastern France through to central Europe. They are distinguished by *O.t.lacteum* having a shorter tubercula pubertatis, segments *xxxi–xxxiv* only, and lacking genital tumescences around setae *a* and *b* on segment *xxii*.

117

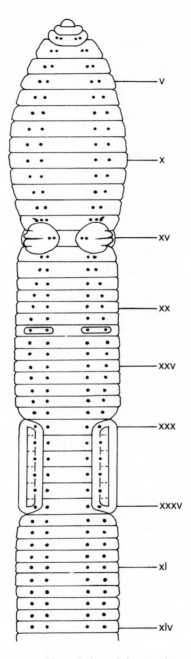

Fig. 41. *Octolasion t. tyrtaeum.* Ventral view of the anterior region.

Genus SATCHELLIUS Gates, 1975

Calciferous sacs opening posteriorly and ventrally into the oesophagus of segment x just in front of septum 10/11. Calciferous lamellae continue along the lateral walls of the sacs. Nephridial vesicles sausage-shaped. Nephridiopores obvious, alternating irregularly and with asymmetry on each side of the body above setal line b. Prostomium epilobous. Pigment red.

Satchellius mammalis (Savigny)
(Fig. 42)

Enterion mammale Savigny, 1826:181.
Helodrilus (Dendrobaena) mammalis: Michaelsen, 1900:493.
Dendrobaena mammalis: Gerard, 1964:36; Bouché, 1972:402.
Satchellius mammalis: Gates, 1975a:1.

Length 24–41 mm, diameter 1.5–3 mm, segment number 83–100. Body cydrindrical with a tendency to become depressed caudally. Colour, red or violet red, markedly iridescent; strongly pigmented.

Prostomium epilobous. First dorsal pore in furrow (4/5) 5/6 (6/7), clearly visible. Spermathecal pores paired in furrows 9/10/11 opening above setal line c. Male pores paired between setal lines bc with large conspicuous oval tumescences stretching across segment xv from $\frac{1}{2}xiv-\frac{1}{2}xvi$, sometimes from furrow 13/14 to furrow 16/17, usually suppressing setae b. Clitellum extends over segments $xxxi-xxxvi$; saddle-shaped reaching down to setal line b. Tubercula pubertatis small, forming only lobular, short paired bands on the ventral margin of the clitellum in segments $xxxiii, xxxiv$ (Fig. 42).

Setae distant, post-clitellar formula $aa:ab:bc:cd:dd = 1.7:1.3:1.3:1:2.3$. Setal tumescences surround setae a, b and c on segments ix (infrequently on xi) also only setae a and b on segments $xxv, xxvi, xxxi, xxxii, xxxv, xxxvi$ (Fig. 42).

Septa 6/7–9/10 feebly muscular. Seminal vesicles, four pairs in segments ix, x, xi, xii.

Capsules: Poorly known, length 1.8–2.7 mm, diameter 1.1–2.7 mm.

Reproduction: Biparental. Spermatophores up to three seen at a time on the ventrum over segments $xxv-xxx$. Chromosome number 34.

Habitat: Under moss and woodland litter, mostly in soils with a high organic content (pH 4.3–8.2) in old pastures, marshy meadows and on river banks.

Distribution: Western Europe: Italy, Spain, France, Belgium, Netherlands, West Germany, Norway.

British records: Widespread, including Eire and the Channel Islands (Guernsey), seldom abundant.

Notes:
Known as little tree worm.

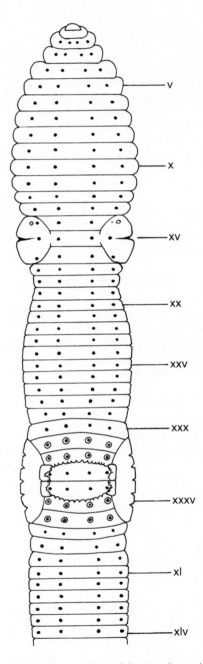

Fig. 42. *Satchellius mammalis*. Ventral view of the anterior region.

Family SPARGANOPHILIDAE Michaelsen, 1928

Body cylindrical but capable of forming a dorsal groove. Dorsal pores sometimes present anteriorly. Setae, 4 pairs on each segment. Clitellum saddle-shaped, occupying 11–13 segments over *xv–xxv* (*xxvi*((*xxvii*); paired tubercula pubertatis present, usually ridge-like. Male pores superficial, paired in furrow 18/19 or on segment *xix*, intra-clitellar. Spermathecal pores paired, occasionally multiple, inconspicuous in furrows 6/7/8/9. Gizzard(s) and calciferous glands absent. Prostate-like glands present, usually 4 pairs, *not* associated with the male pores. Spermathecae adiverticulate. Meganephridial.

Notes:

The family Sparganophilidae contains a single genus accommodating a dozen or more Nearctic species mostly from the southeastern United States. A single species, *Sparganophilus tamesis*, has been recorded on a few occasions in England and once in France.

Sparganophilus tamesis Benham
(Fig. 43)

Sparganophilus tamesis Benham, 1892:156; Jamieson, 1971:812; Bouché, 1972:196; Reynolds, 1980:190.
Sparganophilus eiseni Smith, 1895:142; Reynolds, 1980:191.
Helodrilus elongatus Friend, 1911a:146.
Sparganophilus elongatus: Friend, 1921:137; Cernosvitov, 1942:272; Reynolds, 1980:198.
Pelodrilus cuenoti Tétry, 1934:324.

Length 70–200mm, diameter 1–5mm, segment number 125–260. Dorsal pores usually absent, rarely present in the furrows of the pharyngeal region, i.e. 1/2/3/4/5/6. Spermathecal pores (3 pairs) in furrows 6/7/8/9 above setal line *c*. Female pores paired on segment *xiv*, presetal in *ab* near to setal line *a*. Male pores paired, inconspicuous, presetal on segment *xix* between setal lines *bc* towards the lateral margins of the tubercula pubertatis. Pores of prostate-like glands on several segments *xvii–xxvi* slightly anterolaterally to seta *b*. Clitellum extends over segments (*xiv*) *xv–xxvi* (*xxvii*). Tubercula pubertatis present on most clitellar segments, *xv–xxiv* or at least *xix–xxii* where they form (paired) bands along the ventral edge of the clitellum above setal line *b* (Fig. 43).

Setae closely paired, setae *ab* on segment *xxvi* and adjacent segments, often on paired genital tumescences (Fig. 43).

Habitat: Limicolous, usually in benthic muds of streams, rivers, ponds and lakes or in adjacent saturated soils.

Distribution: Eastern North America from Ontario through to Guatemala; introduced into Britain and France (Lorraine).

British records: River Thames (Goring and Reading), Cheshire meres, Lake

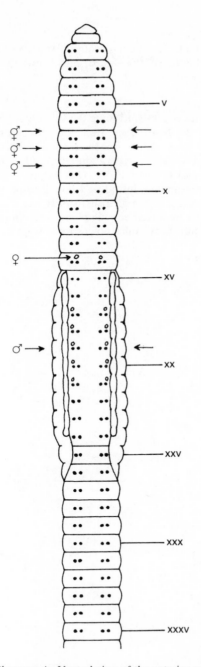

Fig. 43. *Sparganophilus tamesis*. Ventral view of the anterior region.

Windermere and tanks containing water plants: Surrey (Royal Botanic Gardens, Kew), Middlesex (Greenford) and Cornwall (Pencarrow, Washaway, near St. Mabyn).

Notes:

Some European specimens (including the sub-adult types) were separated specifically from the North American populations owing to a misinterpretation of variations due to growth and the diverse effects of differing techniques of fixation and preservation (Reynolds, 1980). There are also minor (?phenotypic) setal differences (Fender, personal communication). The species was seemingly introduced into Europe among the roots of Nearctic water plants as the British records can all be associated with gardens containing imported aquatic plants, e.g. Goring-on-Thames, the type-locality, is only a few miles downstream from the Botanic Gardens, Oxford.

Family GLOSSOSCOLECIDAE Michaelsen, 1900

Body cylindrical. Dorsal pores seldom present. Setae usually 4 pairs on each segment, occasionally with quincunx arrangement, i.e. posteriorly the distance between setal couples alternates on successive segments (*Pontoscolex*); setae rarely numerous (*Periscolex*). Clitellum saddle-shaped occupying up to 12 segments beginning near segment *xiv*, tubercula pubertatis present. Male pores inconspicuous usually intra-clitellar, rarely post-clitellar (*Opisthodrilus*), sometimes within copulatory pouches; exceptionally 2 pairs (*Eudevoscolex*). Spermathecal pores inconspicuous, usually paired seldom multiple, mainly pre-testicular occasionally including the testicular segments. Oesophageal gizzard in segment *vi*, calciferous glands external (extramural), 1–8 pairs between segments *vii–xiv*. Intestinal dilation in the region of segment *xvi*. Prostates or prostate-like glands absent. Spermathecae adiverticulate either interparietal or extending freely into the coelom. Meganephridial.

Notes:

The family Glossoscolecidae contains about 200 species forming 25 genera confined to the litter and soils of the forests of tropical central and South America with the exception of the wide-ranging *Pontoscolex corethrurus*, first recorded in Britain from the Royal Botanic Gardens, Kew by Beddard (1906). Beddard had previously reported other Glossoscolecidae *Diachaeta barbadensis* (Beddard, 1983*a*) and *D. hesperidium* (Beddard, 1893*b*) but they cannot be regarded as British occurring species as they were described from cases of imported soil. They resemble *Pontoscolex corethrurus* but are distinguishable among other characters on the regular arrangement of the setal pairs throughout the body; they differ from each other mainly on the number of pairs of spermathecae.

Pontoscolex corethrurus (F. Müller)
(Fig. 44)

Lumbricus corethrurus (F. Müller) 1856:26.
Pontoscolex corethrurus: Gates, 1972*a*:54.

Length 60–120 mm, diameter 4–6 mm, segment number 90–212 Dorsal pores absent. Prostomium absent but everted buccal tissue may simulate a prostomium or proboscis, segment *i* retractile. Spermathecal pores paired, minute (seldom seen) in furrows 6/7/8/9 in setal line *c*. Female pores paired slits on segment *xiv*, located by furrow 14/15 between setal lines *ab*. Male pores minute (seldom seen) paired in furrow 20/21 nearby to setal line *b*. Clitellum saddle-shaped over segments (*xv*) *xvi–xxii* (*xxiii*) with the tubercula pubertatis forming (paired) longitudinal bands across segments *xix–xxi* (*xxii*) laterally to setal line *b* (Fig. 44a).

Setae closely paired anteriorly becoming gradually wider apart on alternate segments until posteriorly the quincunx arrangement is attained (setal couples being alternately closely and widely paired on successive segments); posterior setae modified, stout distally with rows of fine teeth. Setae *ab* on segments carrying the tubercula pubertatis and adjacent segments, with genital tumescences (Fig. 44a and b).

Internally, the oesophagus has 3 pairs of extra-mural (stalked) calciferous glands in segments *vii*, *viii*, *ix*. Single pair of testes in segment *xi* (metandry) with the seminal vesicles in *xii* extending back for several segments.

Habitat: Litter and soils of the tropical rain forests of South America but frequently found on or near beaches (euryhaline?) and in cultivation including compost.

Distribution: Presumably indigenous to northeastern South America but now occurs sporadically throughout the tropics mainly where exotic crops or new agricultural techniques have been introduced; recorded from greenhouses in temperate regions.

British record: Surrey (Kew).

Notes:

In New Guinea, experiments on feeding and growth rates of pigs showed the animals to have a marked preference for food containing the introduced *Pontoscolex corethrurus* compared with native species when the protein content of their diet was enriched with earthworms.

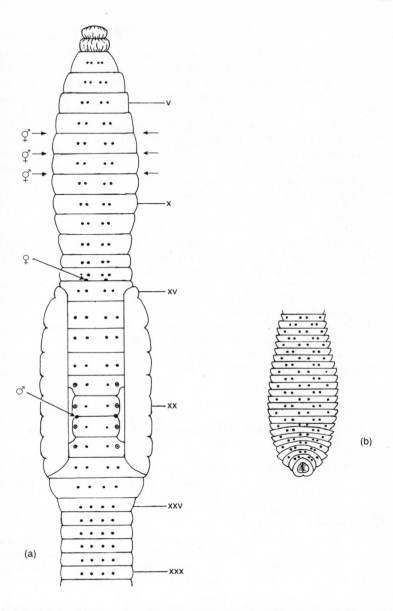

Fig. 44. *Pontoscolex corethrurus*. (*a*) ventral view of the anterior region and (*b*) ventral view of the posterior region showing the quincunx arrangement of the setae.

Family MEGASCOLECIDAE Rosa, 1891

Body cylindrical. Dorsal pores present. Setae commonly 4 pairs on each segment, sometimes numerous. Clitellum annular or saddle-shaped, usually occupying up to 7 segments between segments *xii–xviii*; tubercula pubertatis absent but genital papillae, markings and/or porophores common. Male pores usually on segment *xviii* (rarely *xvii*, *xix* or *xx*), immediately post-clitellar; prostatic pores rare, usually prostatic ducts discharge through male pores. Spermathecal pores paired or multiple, pre-testicular. One to three oesophageal gizzards usually present, intestinal gizzards rare (*Pleinogaster*); stalked (extra-mural) calciferous glands often present. Prostates racemose without central duct. Spermathecae usually diverticulate, paired or numerous. Meganephridial or micronephridial.

Notes:

The family Megascolecidae is represented by over 1000 species forming about 25 genera throughout its wide distribution in the east where it ranges from the eastern USSR to Australasia. A number of species have now spread throughout the tropics and even into greenhouses in temperate regions, especially members of the *Pheretima* group of genera from the rain forests of southern Asia through to Queensland, for example, *Amynthas* and *Metaphire*. A few representatives of two genera have been recorded in greenhouses in the British Isles while species of a third genus were described from imported soil and a species of a fourth genus was deliberately introduced into Scotland in 1975.

Characters of genera of Megascolecidae recorded in the British Isles

Perionyx Perrier, 1872. Setae numerous; first dorsal pore in furrow 4/5 or 5/6; clitellum extending over 4 or more segments (*xiii*, *xiv–xvii*); gizzard(s) and calciferous glands absent; intestinal caeca absent; excretory system meganephridial.

Pheretima group of genera (part): *Amynthas* Kinberg, 1867; *Metaphire* Sims and Easton, 1972. Setae numerous; first dorsal pore in or near furrow 10/11; clitellum restricted to 3 segments (*xiv–xvi*); female pore single, midventral *xiv*; gizzard large in segment *viii*, calciferous glands absent; single pair of intestinal caeca originating in or near segment *xxvii*; excretory system micronephridial.

Spenceriella Michaelsen, 1907. Setae numerous; first dorsal pore in furrow 3/4; clitellum extending over 4 or more segments ($\frac{1}{2}$*xiii*, *xiv–xvii*); gizzard globular in segment *v*; calciferous glands absent; intestinal caeca absent; excretory system micronephridial.

Key to the adults of perichaetine Megascolecidae recorded from Britain

1. First dorsal pore 3/4, 4/5 or 5/6 (clitellum extending over 4 or more segments).. **8**

First dorsal pore at or near 10/11 (clitellum restricted to 3 segments).. **2**

2. Male pores superficial, inconspicuous (*Amynthas*)..................... **3**

Male pores in copulatory pouches (*Metaphire*)......................... **6**

3. 4 pairs of spermathecal pores.. **4**

Less than 4 pairs of spermathecal pores.................................. **5**

4. Genital markings intrasegmental, numerous on pre- or post-clitellar segments............................ *Amynthas corticis* (p. 128)

Genital markings intersegmental, paired 17/18 and/or 18/19, rarely 19/20 .... *Amynthas rodericensis**

5(3) 2 pairs of spermathecal pores (some genital markings single median on segments *vi–viii*) .... *Amynthas morrisi**

3 pairs of spermathecal pores (genital markings paired or in clusters).. *Amynthas gracilis* (p. 130)

6(2) 4 pairs of spermathecal pores................. *Metaphire posthuma**

2 pairs of spermathecal pores **7**

7. Intestinal caeca simple, possibly with incised margins ....
.... *Metaphire californica**

Intestinal caeca manucate with 5 diverticula
*Metaphire schmardae**

8(1) Female pore single median (usually more than 30 setae around each post-clitellar segment)...................*Perionyx excavatus* (p. 134)

Female pores closely paired (usually less than 30 setae around each post-clitellar segment)................... *Spenceriella minor* (p. 136)

*Species not described here, records noted below under *Amynthas* spp. (p. 132) or *Metaphire* spp. (p. 132).

Amynthas corticis (Kinberg)
(Fig. 45)

Perichaeta corticis Kinberg, 1867:102.
Amynthas corticis: Easton, 1986 (in press).
Megascolex diffringens Baird, 1869a:40 & 1869b:387.
Pheretima diffringens: Gates, 1972a:177.
Megascolex indicus Horst, 1883:186
Perichaeta indica: Service, 1890:396; Beddard, 1890:94; Friend, 1891:15.
Perichaeta nipponica Beddard, 1892c:760; Friend, 1910:80.

Length 45–270 mm, diameter 3–6 mm, segment number (79) 105–118 (121). 4 pairs of ventral spermathecal pores 0.3 body circumference apart in furrows 5/6/7/8/9. Male pores paired segment *xviii*, superficial on small porophores. Genital markings small, sometimes numerous on pre- and post-clitellar segments (Fig. 45). Intestinal caeca simple with smooth margins, originating in segment *xxvii*.

Indigenous range: High altitudes in Nepal, northern Pakistan, northern India, Burma and southern China.

British records: Greenhouses: Dumfries and Galloway (Maxwelltown); Cumbria (Kendal); Cheshire (Holmes Chapel); Powys (Machynlleth); Suffolk (Bury St. Edmonds and Woodbridge); Hertfordshire (St. Albans); Surrey (Kew).

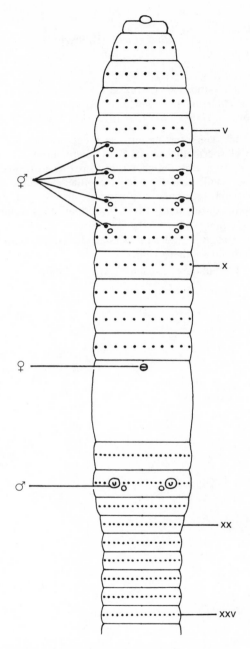

Fig. 45. *Amynthas corticis*. Ventral view of the anterior region.

130

Amynthas gracilis (Kinberg)
(Fig. 46)

Nitocris gracilis Kinberg, 1867:112.
Amynthas gracilis: Easton, 1984 (in press).
Perichaeta hawayana Rosa, 1891:396.
Pheretima hawayana: Gates, 1963:13 & 1972*a*:189.

Length 56–156 mm, diameter 3–6 mm, segment number (70) 91–98 (101). 3 pairs of ventral spermathecae 0.3 body circumference apart in furrows 5/6/7/8. Male pores paired segment *xviii*, superficial on small porophores. Genital markings small, clusters up to 11 papillae median to the male pores and occasionally on segments *xvii* and *xix* also paired median to the spermathecal pores on segments *v–viii*. Intestinal caeca simple with incised margins, originating in segment *xxvii* (Fig. 46).

Indigenous range: High altitudes in Pakistan, India, Bangladesh, Sri Lanka, Burma, Thailand and southern China.

British record: "Greenhouse, England" (Gates, 1963).

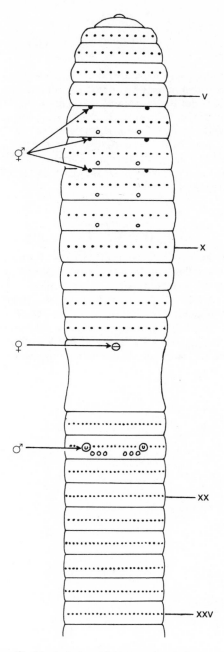

Fig. 46. *Amyntha gracilis*. Ventral view of the anterior region.

Amynthas spp.
(Fig. 47a and b)

In addition to *corticis* and *gracilis*, two other species of the genus *Amynthas* Kinberg, 1867 have been reported from the British Isles but they were found in soil imported into the Royal Botanic Gardens, Kew. The latter although common allochthonous earthworms, cannot be accepted as British occurring species. They were firstly *A. morrisi* (Beddard, 1892*a*:166) originally recorded as *Perichaeta barbadensis* Beddard, 1892*a*:167 and *P. mauritiana* Beddard, 1892*a*:170 and secondly *a. rodericensis* (Grube, 1879:554) originally recorded as *Perichaeta dyeri* Beddard, 1892*a*:157 and *P. sinensis* Beddard, 1892*a*:157.

Metaphire spp.
(Fig. 47, c, d, e)

Three species of the genus *Metaphire* Sims and Easton, 1972 have been reported from imported soil at the Royal Botanic Gardens, Kew but cannot be regarded as British occurring species. They were *M. californica* (Kinberg, 1867:102) reported as *Perichaeta hesperidum* Beddard, 1892*a*:169; *M. posthuma* (Vaillant, 1868:228) reported by Beddard (1906:66) and *M. schmardae* (Horst, 1883:194) among specimens (mis)identified as *Perichaeta sumatrana* by Beddard, 1892*a*:155 (Easton, 1986). *M. californica*, *M. posthuma* and *M. schmardae* are wide ranging allochthonous species.

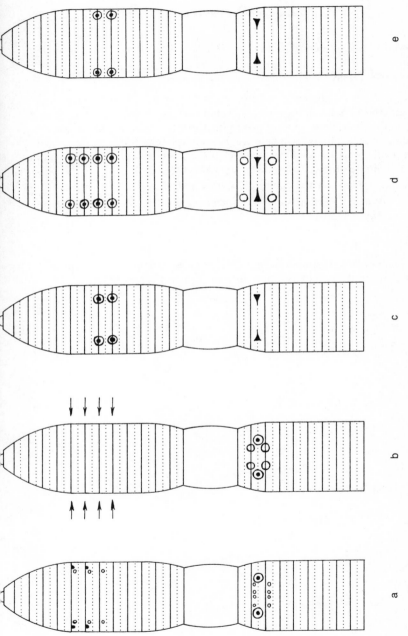

Fig. 47. *Amynthas* sp. and *Metaphire* sp. Ventral view of the anterior region. (*a*) *Amynthas morrisi*, (*b*) *Amynthas rodericensis*. (*c*) *Metaphire californica*, (*d*) *Metaphire posthuma* and (*e*) *Metaphire schmardae*.

Perionyx excavatus Perrier
(Fig. 48)

Perionyx excavatus Perrier, 1872:126; Gates, 1972*a*:141; Easton, 1986 (in press).
Perionyx sp. Friend, 1911*a*:188.

Length 30–180 mm, diameter 3–7 mm, segment number 123–178. Two pairs of spermathecal pores in furrows 7/8/9 about the same distance apart as the male pores. Male pores closely paired on segment *xviii* on small tranverse protuberances within a single field, each is anterolateral to the tips of penial setae; penial setae in groups of 4–6 each up to 0.6 mm long with many rings and long thin teeth but with indistinct smooth tip (Fig. 48).

Indigenous range: Indian, southern Oriental and Malaysian regions.

British records: Hertfordshire (Harpenden and St. Albans); London (Chelsea Physic Garden).

Notes:

Tolerant of low pH situations, this species has been employed in the breakdown of pig slurry and as a protein source mainly for livestock.

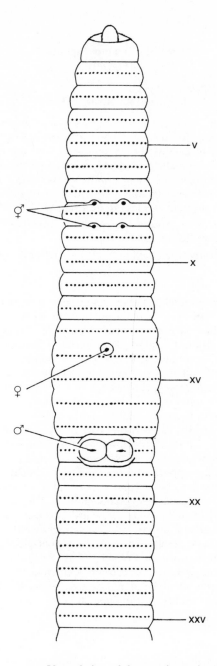

Fig. 48. *Perionyx excavatus*. Ventral view of the anterior region.

136

Spenceriella minor (Spencer)
(Fig. 49)

Megascolex minor Spencer, 1900:49.
Spenceriella minor: Jamieson and Wampler, 1979:640.

Length 38–120 mm, diameter 1.5–3.0 mm, segment number 99–151. Spermathecal pores inconspicuous, two pairs in furrows 7/8/9 opening within setal lines *ab* near to *a*. Male pores combined with the prostatic pores as transverse slits each on a low porophore on *xviii* near to setal line *a*. Genital markings paired on segments *x* and *xviii* near setal lines *b* and *c*, also single median on *xvii* and *xix* also possibly *xx* but may be imperfectly paired. 25–30 setae around each segment, seldom more (Fig. 49).

Indigenous range: New South Wales and Queensland, Australia (also recorded Lord Howe Island and New Zealand).

British records: Strathclyde (Lephinmore, District of Argyll and Bute).

Notes:
Introduced into Scotland in 1975 in an attempt to initiate the decomposition of blanket peat for land reclamation in an agricultural utilization scheme. Since then the numbers of *S. minor* have increased slowly but with indiscernible soil improvement. The species may have been one of five Megascolecidae introduced from Mount Kosciusko, southeastern New South Wales, the others were possibly *Cryptodrilus fastigatus* Fletcher, 1889, *Diporochaeta frenchi* (Spencer, 1892), *Notoscolex montiskosciuskoi* Jamieson, 1973 and *Spenceriella celmisiae* Jamieson, 1973 but they seemingly failed to become established. Mount Kosciusko at 2230 m is the highest peak in Australia. It forms part of the Australian Alps and was formerly extensively glaciated, nowadays it is snow-capped in winter and has become a popular ski resort. With other peaks in the Australian Alps, Mount Kosciusko supports the only alpine herbfield on the Australian mainland and thereby having the potentiality to harbour a cold-adapted endemic fauna (Jamieson, 1973). Though the soil acidities and high rainfall in alpine herbfield are similar to typical Scottish highland conditions, undecomposed organic matter has not accumulated and peaty podzols have not developed, possibly through the beneficial soil forming activities of megascolecid earthworms (Wood, 1974). Several of the cold-tolerant Australian species were introduced into Lephinmore to examine whether these larger worms would be more effective decomposers than the smaller native species of Lumbricidae in Scottish peat.

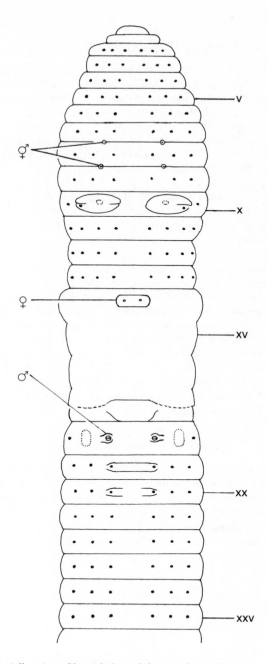

Fig. 49. *Spenceriella minor*. Ventral view of the anterior region.

Family OCNERODRILIDAE Beddard, 1891

Body cylindrical. Dorsal pores seldom present. Setae 4 pairs on each segment. Clitellum annular or saddle-shaped, usually occupying up to 7 segments between segments *xii–xix* (exceptionally extending back a further 7 segments to *xxvi*, *Nematogenia*); tubercula pubertatis absent but genital papillae and/or porophores common. Male pores paired *xvii* or *xviii*, rarely *xix* or *xx*, commonly intra-clitellar or by the posterior margin of the clitellum; prostatic pores 1–3 pairs between *xvi–xxi*. Spermathecal pores pre-testicular. One or two oesophageal gizzards usually present, intestinal gizzards absent; calciferous glands either absent (Malabarinae) or a single medioventral pouch or paired stalked laterdorsal glands in segment *ix* and/or *x* (Ocnerodrilinae). Last hearts in segment *xi*. Prostates tubular with central duct. Spermathecae seldom diverticulate, extending freely into the coelom. Meganephridial.

Notes:

(1) Members of this family are often small and associated with freshwater.

(2) The subfamily Ocnerodrilinae occurs throughout most of the tropical Americas, tropical and southern Africa to Madagascar and the Seychelles while the subfamily Malabarinae is found in peninsular India and nearby areas. A few allochthonous ocnerodriline species have such wide ranges in the tropics that their geographical origins are uncertain.

(3) Friend (1916:147) described a species from the lily tank in the Botanic Garden, Oxford while previously Beddard (1892*a*; 1893*a* & *b*) described seven new species from soil imported from Africa into the Royal Botanic Garden, Kew. None has been recorded again from the British Isles and indeed all are rare in temperate regions.

Genus EUKERRIA Michaelsen, 1935

Male pores paired segment *xviii*. Two pairs of prostatic pores, segments *xvii* and *xix*. Two pairs of spermathecal pores, furrows 7/8/9. One gizzard in segment *vii*, calciferous glands paired, laterodorsal in segment *ix*. Testes proandric (one pair in segment *x* only).

British record: Oxford, species described as *Kerria rubra* sp. nov. by Friend, 1916 (= ?*eiseniana* Rosa, 1895; Cernosvitov, 1942:267).

139

Genus GORDIODRILUS Beddard, 1892

Male pores paired, usually on segment *xviii* associated with the seminal grooves joining the prostatic pores. Two pairs of prostatic pores in adjacent segments, usually *xvii* and *xviii*, sometimes *xviii* and *xix* (rarely *xix* and *xx* or *xx* and *xxi*). Two pairs of spermathecal pores, furrows 7/8/9. Gizzard absent; calciferous gland as a single medioventral pouch in segment *ix*. Testes holandric (two pairs, segments *x* and *xi*).

British records: Five species were described as new to science by Beddard, 1892*b* (*elegans, ditheca, dominicensis, robustus, tenuis*) in soil imported into Kew Gardens, Surrey.

Genus NANNODRILUS Beddard, 1894

Male pores paired segment *xviii*. Two pairs of prostatic pores, segment *xvii* and *xix*. Single pair of spermathecal pores, furrow 7/8. Two gizzards, segments *vii* and *viii*; calciferous gland as a single medioventral pouch in segment *ix*. Testes holandric (two pairs, segments *x* and *xi*).

British record: Imported soil, Kew Gardens, Surrey; species described as *Ilyogenia africana* sp. nov. by Beddard, 1893*b*:703.

Genus NEMATOGENIA Eisen, 1900

Male pores combined with a single pair of prostatic pores segment *xvii*. Single pair of spermathecal pores, furrow 8/9. Two small gizzards, segments *vi* and *vii*; calciferous glands paired, laterodorsal in segment *ix*. Testes metandric (one pair in segment *xi* only).

British record: Imported soil, Kew Gardens, Surrey; species described as *Ocnerodrilus lacuum* sp. nov. by Beddard, 1893*a*:259.

Family ACANTHODRILIDAE Claus, 1880

Body cylindrical. Dorsal pores usually present. Setae commonly 4 pairs on each segment, sometimes 5 or 6 pairs or numerous. Clitellum annular or saddle-shaped frequently occupying up to 6 or 7 segments between segments *xii–xviii*; tubercula pubertatis absent but genital papillae, markings or porophores common. Male pores either paired on segment *xviii* with paired prostatic pores on segments *xvii* and *xix,* or, paired on segment *xvii* or *xix* with a single pair of prostatic pores on the same segment or combined; commonly located by the posterior margin of the clitellum. Spermathecal pores pre-testicular. One to three oesophageal gizzards occasionally rudimentary or absent, intestinal gizzards absent; stalked (extra-mural) calciferous glands common. Last hearts (or equivalents) behind segment *xi*. Prostates tubular with central duct. Spermathecae usually diverticulate. Meganephridial.

Notes:

The most widespread of all earthworm families, Acanthodrilidae occur in the central and western Nearctic and apart from Antarctica, throughout the southern hemisphere. Represented in the British Isles by a single species.

Microscolex phosphoreus (Dugès)
(Fig. 50)

Lumbricus phosphoreus Dugès, 1837:17.
Microscolex phosphoreus: Gates, 1972a:35; Bouché, 1972:183.
Length 10–35 mm, diameter 1.0–1.5 mm, segment number 73–88 (90). Setae 4 pairs on each segment. Dorsal pores absent. Clitellum annular occupying segments *xiii–xvii*, sometimes incomplete ventrally on the first and last segments where saddle-shaped. Male and prostatic pores both paired on segment *xvii* between setal lines *a* and *b*: the male pores by setal line *a* and the prostatic pores near to setal line *b*; penial setae present between the male and prostatic pores. Spermathecal pores, single pair in furrow 8/9 (Fig. 50). Gizzard rudimentary in segment *v*, calciferous glands absent. Testes holandric (paired in segments *x* and *xi*).

Indigenous range: South America, south of the Tropic of Capricorn.

British records: Market gardens in Nottinghamshire (Friend, 1913a:24), Jersey and Worcestershire (Beddard, 1899:52; Friend, 1913b:459) also under compost, Dublin.

(1) Species of the genus *Microscolex* inhabit the temperate and subtropical areas of southern South America and islands of the southern oceans.

(2) Two species, *dubius* and *phosphoreus*, have spread to many other areas including South Africa, Australasia, North and Central America and Europe but only *phosphoreus* has so far been introduced into the British Isles. The two species are readily separable on the larger size and absence of spermathecae in *dubius* and (especially at night) the marked phorescence of *phosphoreus* when disturbed.

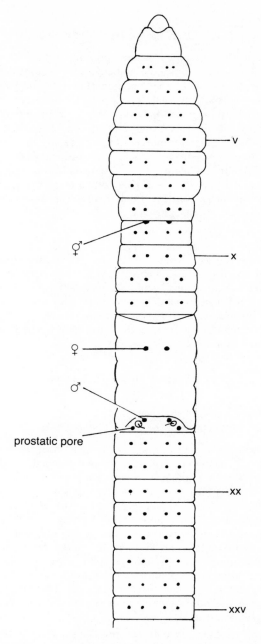

Fig. 50. *Microscolex phosphoreus*. Ventral view of the anterior region.

Family OCTOCHAETIDAE Michaelsen, 1900

Body cylindrical. Dorsal pores usually present. Setae 4 pairs on each segment. Clitellum annular or saddle-shaped usually occupying 6–7 segments between segments *xii–xviii*; tubercula pubertatis absent, genital papillae and/or porophores common. Male pores paired mainly either on segment *xviii* with paired prostatic pores on both *xvii* and *xix*, or, on *xvii*, *xviii* or *xix* with a single pair of prostatic pores on the same segment or combined; located usually at the posterior margin of the clitellum, rarely intra-clitellar. Spermathecal pores pre-testicular. One to three oesophageal gizzards usually present, occasionally rudimentary or absent, intestinal gizzards absent; stalked (extra-mural) calciferous glands common. Last hearts (or equivalents) behind segment *xi*. Prostates tubular with central duct. Spermathecae usually diverticulate. Micronephridial.

Notes:
  A family comprising two groups, temperate species inhabiting Australasia and tropical species in the Americas, Africa and peninsular India into Burma. Species of the tropical genus *Dichogaster* have been reported from most parts of the world including the British Isles where too the species *Eutyphaeus nicholsoni* and *Trigaster minima* were described from imported soil in the Royal Botanic Gardens, Kew by Beddard, 1901 and Friend, 1911*b* respectively.

Dichogaster bolaui (Michaelsen)
(Fig. 51)

Benhamia bolavi (lapsus) Michaelsen, 1891:9.
Dichogaster bolaui: Michaelsen, 1900:340; Gates, 1972*a*:279.

Length 20–40 mm, diameter 1–3 mm, segment number 70–90. First dorsal in furrows 5/6/7. Clitellum annular occupying segments (*xiii*) *xiv–xviii* (*xix*) (*xx*) (*xxi*), often thinner midventrally. Male pores paired on segment *xviii* discharging into the seminal grooves joining the paired prostatic pores in segments *xvii* and *xix* at the level of setal line *a*. Penial setae present, up to 0.4 mm long, hooked or flattened distally, ornamented. Female pore single, on a papilla midventral on segment *xiv* sometimes extending beyond setal lines *aa*. Two pairs of spermathecal pores in furrows 7/8/9 near setal line *a* (Fig. 51). Two gizzards partly fused to form a large, single bipartite structure, location difficult to determine accurately but seemingly originating in segments *vi* and *vii*. Three pairs of stalked calciferous glands laterodorsal in segments *xv, xvi*, and *xvii*. Testes holandric (paired in segments *x* and *xi*).

Indigenous range: Indian subcontinent into Burma and (?) Malaya.
British records: Friend (1916:265) described the species *Dichogaster*

143

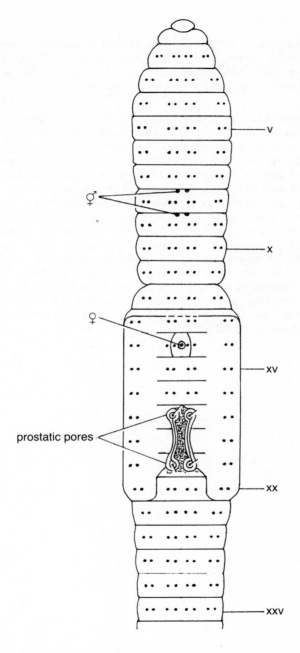

Fig. 51. *Dichogaster bolaui*. Ventral view of the anterior region.

lageniformis from the Botanic Gardens, Oxford. It was poorly characterized and its identity cannot be established (Cernosvitov, 1942:268). However, since it was a small quadriprostatic worm, it may have been the most widespread and commonest species of the genus, *Dichogaster bolaui*.

Notes:

Dichogaster bolaui has now spread through to Australasia and on to many Pacific islands; in addition, it is widespread in tropical Africa and the Americas also in greenhouses in temperate regions.

Another species, *Dichogaster saliens* with almost the same wide distributions, was described by Beddard (1893*b*) from soil imported into the Royal Botanic Gardens, Kew from Penang and Singapore. It is separable from *bolaui* on several characters: *saliens* is somewhat larger (17–70 mm) and has a single pair of prostatic pores on segment *xvii* with the paired male pores opening into furrow 17/18 (penial setae with a knob-like tip), female pores are closely paired just median to setae *aa* on segment *xiv*; internally the gizzards appear to originate in segments *vii* and *viii*.

A third species, *Dichogaster crassa*, was also described by Beddard (1893*b*) from soil imported into the Royal Botanic Gardens, Kew but from Nigeria where the species appears to be endemic. (Although quadriprostatic, among other characters it is separable from *bolaui* by having paired female pores near setal lines *bb*.)

Family EUDRILIDAE Claus, 1880

Body cylindrical. Dorsal pores absent. Setae 4 pairs on each segment, frequently with the ventral couple more widely paired than the dorsal couple. Clitellum annular or saddle-shaped, often occupying 6–8 segments between segments *xii–xviii*; tubercula pubertatis absent but genital papillae and/or porophores common. Male pore(s) single or paired on segment *xvii* or *xviii* or in furrow 17/18, combined with the prostatic pore(s); usually located by the posterior margin of the clitellum. Penial setae sometimes present. Spermathecal pore(s) single or paired usually post-testicular, sometimes combined with the (paired) female pores. Single oesophageal gizzard commonly in segment *v*, rarely reduced or absent when intestinal gizzards often present; calciferous glands absent (Pareudrilinae) or present (Eudrilinae) when paired and stalked either in *xiii* with single suboesophageal pouches in segments *ix*, *x* and *xi*, or, paired and stalked in *xii* with single suboesophageal pouches in *x* and *xi*. Testes free (Pareudrilinae) or vasa deferentia entally continuous with the seminal vesicles and enclosing the testes (Eudrilinae). Prostates tubular with simple central duct but commonly modified with enlarged central chamber becoming acorn-shaped ('euprostates'). Spermathecae absent but replaced either by a system of coelomic ducts leading from the spermathecal pore(s) to the oviducts, or, the spermathecal and female pores combining with modifications to the (?) ovisacs and ental regions of the oviducts (*Eudrilus*). Meganephridial.

Notes:

A family mainly of the forests of central Africa. One species, *Eudrilus eugeniae*, has been introduced into many other parts of the world including greenhouses in temperate regions.

Beddard (1891 & 1893*b*) described new genera and species from African soil imported into the Royal Botanic Gardens, Kew (*Eudriloides durbanensis, Heliodrilus lagosensis* and *Hyperiodrilus africanus*). None has subsequently been recorded from outside of the African continent and cannot be regarded as British occurring species. Among other characters, they are distinguishable from *Eudrilus eugeniae* on the male and spermathecal pores being single median (the latter being separate from the paired, lateral female pores).

Eudrilus eugeniae (Kinberg)
(Fig. 52)

Lumbricus eugeniae Kinberg, 1867:98.
Eudrilus eugeniae: Gates, 1972a:51.

Length (32) 90–140 (185)mm, diameter 5–8mm. Segment number 145–196 (211). Setae closely paired. Clitellum annular between segments (*xiii*) xiv–xviii, less strongly developed ventrally. Male and prostatic pores paired, combined, large, immediately in front of furrow 17/18 between setal lines *ab*; penial setae absent. Female and spermathecal pores paired, combined, moderately sized transverse slits centred at or just median to setal lines *cc*, presetal on segment *xiv*. Gizzard in segment *v*; two midventral sub-oesophageal pouches in segments *x* and *xi* with paired stalked (extra-mural) calciferous glands laterodorsal in segment *xii*. Testes holandric (paired in segments *x* and *xi*). Paired ovaries in segment *xiii* with the ovisacs and/or ental ends of the oviducts modified to form (paired) spermathecae.

Indigenous range: Western Africa.

British record: Kew, Surrey (Beddard, 1906).

Notes:
(1) Known as African night crawler.
(2) The species has been spread by man eastwards from Africa to India and on to New Zealand and westwards into tropical America especially the islands of the Atlantic and Caribbean. It has also colonized much of the Southern United States where it is farmed and known as the African night-crawler. Intolerant of temperatures below 50°F, this species requires temperatures of 70–80°F for reproduction.

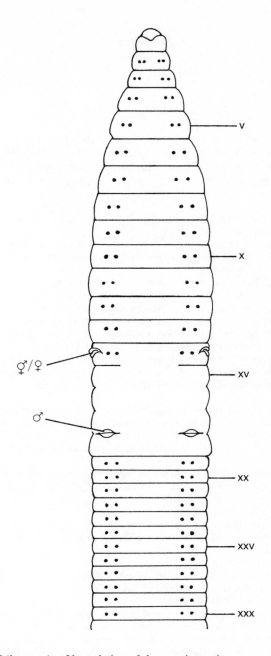

Fig. 52. *Eudrilus eugeiae*. Ventral view of the anterior region.

Glossary

The principal authorities consulted in the preparation of this glossary were: for specialized terms relating mainly to earthworms, Stephenson (1930) and Gates (1972*a*); for terms having a wider usage in zoology, Leftwich (1967), Godman and Payne (1979) and Lincoln, Boxshall and Clark (1982).

aclitellate Without a clitellum, due usually to immaturity, seldom to regression following a period of sexual activity.

aestivation A period of quiescence, i.e. inactivity or dormancy, during summer or drought when a worm becomes torpid and, to prevent dehydration, coils up in a chamber often deep in the soil.

adventitious Accidental, occurring in an unusual habitat or host.

afferent (blood) vessel Vessel supplying blood to an organ or structure.

afforestation Tree planting, the establishment of new plantations.

albuminous Containing albumen, i.e. a solution of protein and water.

allochthonous Exogenous, non-native, originating outside and transported into an area, either deliberately or accidentally, *cf.* autochthonous.

amphimictic Obligatory biparental sexual reproduction with the fertilization of the female gamete (ovum) by a male gamete (spermatozöon), *cf.* parthenogenesis.

ampulla (*pl.* **ampullae**) Dilated ental region of a spermatheca forming a distal chamber.

anecic In earthworms, deep-dwelling species that come up to the soil surface to feed or obtain food and to breed. From *anekas* (Greek) = upward, reach up, come up to, *cf.* endogean, epigean.

annular Clitellum encircling the body, being continuous ventrally, *cf.* saddle-shaped.

annulus (*pl.* **annuli**) An external, superficial ring formed by a secondary furrow around a segment; commonly two secondary furrows occur, one on either side of the setal area, producing a triannulate condition.

anthropochorous Transported by man.

anus Posterior opening of the gut (alimentary canal).

apomorphic Derived structure, recently acquired during the evolution of a taxon, *cf.* pleisiomorphic.

arboreal Tree-dwelling.

atrophy The diminution in size and in function of an organ, especially caused by lack of use or from a pathological condition, *cf.* hypertrophy.

austral Southern, *cf.* boreal.

autochthonous Endogenous, native, produced within a given region, *cf.* allochthonous.

autofecundity Self-fertilization (in hermaphrodite animals).

autotomy Self amputation; in earthworms, shedding the caudal region.

biparental True sexual reproduction involving two individuals with the union of the gametes, *cf.* amphimictic.

boreal Northern, *cf.* austral.

buccal cavity The chamber with the mouth as an aperture, often the anteriormost region of the alimentary canal, *cf.* pharynx.

calciferous glands Oesophageal glands controlling the pH balance of the gut and the regulation of the calcium level of the blood; absent from true aquatic earthworms: sometimes termed 'Glands of Morren'.

capsule Egg case (oöphore) secreted by the clitellum, containing several eggs but usually only one embryo completes development to emerge as a hatchling: often termed 'cocoon'.

caudal Pertaining to the posterior region of the body of an earthworm. (Strictly the caudal region of an animal is the part of the body between the anus and the posterior extremity, i.e. the tip of the tail or fin, so properly the term should not be applied to the hinder parts of the bodies of the animals such as earthworms that have a terminal anus.)

cellulase An enzyme involved in the degradation of cellulose.

cerebral ganglia The large, supra-oesophageal, closely applied, paired ganglia situated on the dorsal surface of the pharnyx and connected to the main ventral nerve cord by a 'collar' formed of two commissures. (Evolutionarily, the fore-runner of the so-called 'brain' of insects.)

chaeta (*pl.* **chaetae**) From *kaetos* (Greek) = bristle, *see* seta.

chitin A horny substance forming the setae of earthworms and the cuticle of insects and other arthropoda. It is an aminopolysaccharide and resists most solvent agents.

chitinase A chitinolytic enzyme involved in the degradation of chitin.

chlorogogenous cells Yellow pigmented cells formed around the gut. They break loose and float in the coelomic fluid where they absorb nitrogenous waste substances. Most break up and their remains are engulfed by amoeboid cells that carry them to a nephrostome to be excreted, others enter the tissues of the body where they deposit their pigment or are wafted posteriorly (via mid-ventral foramena in the septa) to the caudal region for storage until autotomy.

circular muscle The outer layer of muscles of the body wall with the fibres encircling the underlying longitudinal muscle.

circumpharyngeal commissures (**connectives**) The two halves of the nerve collar surrounding the oesophagus and linking the ventral nerve cord with the cerebral ganglia.

clitellate Possessing a clitellum, *cf.* aclitellate.

clitellum Saddle-shaped, occasionally annular, region of the body wall formed from several layers of highly glandular epidermal cells (suborder Lumbricina); it secretes mucus from which the egg capsule is formed, provides nourishment for the developing embryos and, in some species, forms a belt-like sheath to encircle and hold together two worms during copulation.

cocoon *See* capsule.

coelom Fluid filled body cavity lined by the peritoneum, embryologically derived from a vacuole in the mesoderm.

commensalism Symbiosis in which one species derives benefit from a common food supply whilst the other species is not adversely affected, *cf.* parasitization, symbiosis.

commissural vessels Paired segmental lateral blood vessels passing from the dorsal vessel to join, at least in a few anterior segments, the ventral vessel or more posteriorly the sub-neural vessel.

compressed Flattened laterally in the dorso-ventral plane, *cf.* depressed.

150

concopulant Mate, partner during copulation.

copulation Sexual intercourse or congress, mating, coition, coitus etc. with (in earthworms) usually the mutual interchange of sperm.

crop A dilation of the alimentary canal where food may be stored for a time before passing to the gizzard, in earthworms described only in members of the family Lumbricidae at the anterior end of the intestine.

cuticle Non-cellular, transparent, tough protective tissue covering the epidermis.

deforestation Wide-scale felling of trees, change in land utilization with the removal of forests (usually) for conversion to arable land.

depressed Flattened dorsoventrally in the lateral plane, *cf.* compressed.

dermis The lower layer of the skin below the epidermis.

diapause A period of inactivity which if *facultative* is controlled by external factors and may be started by injury or adverse changes in the environment (*see* quiescence); if *obligatory* is mainly independent of the environment and provides a period of rest (often for growth or when associated with autotomy, repair). Diapause cannot be terminated until certain physiological events have been completed during a diapause development period (*cf.* quiescence).

dimorphic A species with two genetically determined morphs, i.e. morphological phases.

diploid Having a double set of homologous chromosomes derived from the fusion of the gametes at fertilization, *cf.* haploid and polyploid.

distal Distant, away from the point of attachment, *cf.* proximal.

diurnal variation A biological rhythm having a periodicity of about one day in length: circadian rhythm.

diverticulum (*pl.* **diverticula**) An elongate sac or blind tube, for instance leading from the duct of the spermatheca in many megascolecoid earthworms.

dorsal pore A mid-dorsal, sphinctered aperture leading from the coelom to the exterior in all but the anteriormost furrows in the members of some earthworm families, e.g. Lumbricidae.

dorsal (blood) vessel or **trunk** The large, median blood vessel lying above the gut and sometimes contractile that receives blood from the tissues and organs and conveys it forwards to the (contractile) lateral commissures.

ectal Outermost: as applied to a duct, the external region, *cf.* ental.

efferent (blood) vessel The vessel conveying blood from an organ or structure.

egg-capsule *See* capsule.

embryo An early stage of development leading from a fertilized egg or zygote until the formation of the principal organs, *cf.* hatchling.

endemic Native or restricted to a particular area; breeding in a region but not necessarily originating in that region, *see* indigenous, autochthonous, *cf.* allochthonous.

endogean (Strictly) an interstitial soil organism; in earthworms, species living and feeding in or immediately below the root mat of the vegetation; endogeic, endogeal, endogeous, *cf.* anecic, epigean.

endogenous Autochthonous, *cf.* exogenous, allochthonous.

ental Innermost: as applied to a duct, the internal region, *cf* ectal.

epidermis The outer layer of the skin, derived from the embryonic ectoderm; in earthworms, highly glandular.

epididymus In some earthworms, a coiling in the ental region of the vas deferens usually in the segment behind the funnel.

epigean Living or growing at or above the soil surface; epigeic, epigeal, epigeous, *cf.* anecic, endogean.

epilobous Referring to a prostomium that is continued by a tongue into the peristomium but without reaching the first furrow (1/2).

Euramerica The continent formed in the late Mesozoic before the opening of the north Atlantic, comprising the part of the Laurasia between the Mid-continental Seaway separating present-day eastern from western North America and the Turgai Straits separating present-day Europe from Asia.

euryhaline Able to tolerate wide variations in osmotic pressure, i.e. can withstand varying salinities.

exogenous Allochthonous, *cf.* endogenous, autochthonous.

extra-mural calciferous glands Calciferous glands located externally on the oesophagus, commonly stalked.

facultative Contingent: assuming a particular role or mode of life but not restricted to that condition, *cf.* obligatory.

fertilization The union of the male and female gametes to form a zygote.

fimbriated funnel Funnel with a filamentous fringe around the opening to facilitate the entry of sperm or ova.

furrow An external groove around the body of an earthworm between two adjacent segments.

ganglion (*pl.* **ganglia**) A compact mass of nerve cells.

genital seta An enlarged seta of functional importance during copulation, usually surrounded by a genital tumescence.

genital tumescence In the Lumbricidae, an area of modified epidermis without distinct boundaries and through which a follicle of a genital seta opens.

geophagus Soil feeding, ingesting soil from which organic fragments, micro-flora and -fauna and other microscopic organisms are digested.

gizzard Part of the alimentary canal having thick muscular walls, its main function is to grind up food before it reaches the intestine.

glands of Morren *See* calciferous glands.

gonads The reproductive organs, testes and ovaries, producing the gametes or reproductive cells.

Gondwana (Gondwanaland) The huge Mesozoic southern continent separated by the epicontinental Tethys Sea from the northern continent of Laurasia after the break up of the single Palaeozoic continent of Pangaea.

haemoglobin A red, iron-based respiratory pigment, *haem,* combined with a blood protein, *globin.* In earthworms, haemoglobin occurs in solution in the blood serum unlike in the higher vertebrates where it is confined to corpuscles.

haploid Having a single set of chromosomes or gametic number, i.e. half the number of a fertilized egg or zygote, *cf.* diploid and polyploid.

hatchling The young, small worm that emerges from a capsule.

hermaphrodite Having both male and female reproductive organs in a single individual.

heterozygous Having two different alleles at a given locus of a chromosome pair, *cf.* homozygous.

hibernation Dormancy during the winter, a state of complete, prolonged inactivity; especially in a few mammals when the body temperature drops almost to that of the surroundings, the period usually being preceded by the deposition of body fat to act as a food reserve.

holandry In earthworms: the presence of two pairs of testes, one pair in segment *x* and another pair in segment *xi*, *cf.* proandry, metandry.

holarctic region A zoogeographical region comprising the palaearctic and nearctic regions.

holonephridium *See* meganephridium.

homoiothermic Having a constant body temperature independent of, and usually above, that of the surrounding medium, *cf.* poikilothermic.

homozygous Having identical alleles at a given locus of a chromosome pair, *cf.* heterozygous.

hypertrophy Excessive growth of tissue or of an organ, *cf.* atrophy.

immature A full grown young worm without the clitellum or sexual organs fully developed (often termed *adolescent*), *see* aclitellate.

indigenous Native, originating in a particular area, *see* endemic, autochthonous, *cf.* allochthonous.

intestine The main part of the gut where food is digested and nutrients absorbed; in earthworms, between the hind end of the oesophagus and the anus.

intra-mural calciferous glands Calciferous glands formed in the oesophageal wall of members of the family Lumbricidae.

juvenile An immature, young worm yet to achieve full size.

***K*-selected species** A species characteristic of a relatively constant or predictable environment, typically with slow development, relatively high competitive ability, late reproduction, large body size and iteroparity, i.e. factors that favour the competitive ability of their progeny, *cf. r*-selected species.

lateral commissure(s) Paired segmental blood vessels conveying the blood latero-ventrally from the dorsal vessel to the ventral vessel or sub-neural vessel, when contractile known as lateral hearts.

lateral heart *See* lateral commissure/commissural vessel.

Laurasia The huge Mesozoic northern continent separated by the epicontinental Tethys Sea from the southern continent of Gondwana following the break up of the single Palaeozoic continent of Pangaea.

limicolous Inhabiting mud, shore dwelling.

limnic (limnetic) Pertaining to lakes or to other bodies of standing fresh water; often used with reference only to the open water of a lake away from the bottom.

limnicolous Living in lakes.

longevity The life span of an individual or group of animals.

longitudinal muscle The inner layer of muscles of the body wall between the outer, circular muscles and the peritoneum lining the coelomic cavity; the muscle fibres lie longitudinally.

lumbricine When relating to setae, describing the setal condition of members of the family Lumbricidae with four pairs of setae on each segment (octochaetine), *cf.* perichaetine.

lumen The cavity of a duct, sac, gland or of the gut.

macrolecithal (An egg) with a large yolk, i.e. with a copious food supply mainly of lecithin, a phospho-lipoid substance, *cf.* microlecithal.

macrophagous Feeding on relatively large food particles; in earthworms, consuming grass and (fallen) leaves; macrophage, macrophagy, *cf.* mesophageous, microphagous.

maturation The attainment of sexual maturity, the differentiation of the reproductive cells into viable gametes.

mature Full-grown in breeding condition, adult, (in earthworms) clitellate.

meganephridium One of a pair of large nephridia often known as holonephridia, in each segment of the body except for the first and the last segments, *see* nephridium, *cf.* micronephridium.

meronephridium *See* micronephridium.

mesophagous Feeding on intermediate sized food particles; in earthworms, browsing on the fauna and flora of leaf litter and consuming leaf fragments; mesophage, mesophagy, *cf.* macrophagous, microphagous.

metabolism The synthetic and degradative biochemical processes taking place within an organism.

metamere A segment of the body containing representatives of some or all of the organ systems of the body.

metandry In earthworms: the presence of a single pair of testes in segment *xi*, *cf.* holandry, proandry.

microlecithal (An egg) with a small amount of yolky material, i.e. requiring the developing embryo to obtain an alternative supply of food, in earthworms receiving nourishment from the mucus contained in the capsule.

micronephridium One of many small nephridia also known as a meronephridia occurring in a segment where they may cover the parietal surface of the body wall also often the septa and some segmental organs. Although essentially comprised of tubules with an excretory function, details of structure vary; some may discharge directly onto the body surface, others may lead into a sinus which discharges to the exterior through pores by the setal ring while in some cases the tubules coalesce to form ducts that pass posteriorly before discharging onto the body surface or into the lumen of the intestine.

microphagous Feeding on relatively minute particles; in earthworms, ingesting soil and extracting nourishment from the contained microfauna and -flora; microphage, microphagy, *cf.* macrophagous, mesophagous.

Mid-continental Seaway A late Mesozoic epicontinental sea passing north-south down what is now North America, separating the present day eastern states from the western states and preceding the complete opening of the North Atlantic about 40 Mya, *see* Euramerica.

nearctic region A zoogeographical region comprising Greenland, North America and northern Mexico.

neotropical region A zoogeographical region extending south from the Mexican plateau throughout Central America, the Caribbean and South America.

nephridium (*pl.* **nephridia**) Excretory organ, paired in most segments (holonephridium or meganephridium) comprising a ciliated funnel or nephrostome opening into the preceding segment and leading into a system of tubules richly supplied with blood vessels terminating (usually) in a vesicle or bladder before discharging to the exterior through a nephridiopore in the body wall (often midlaterally in the anterior wall of a furrow); functionally analogous to the vertebrate kidney.

nephridiopore Pore through which the excretory products of the nephridium are discharged to the exterior, sometimes termed *nephropore*.

nephrostome The funnel-like ental extremity of the nephridial tubules opening in the coelom of the preceding segment to the (mega)nephridium.

neurosecretory hormone Chemical secreted by the large, anterior ganglia, commonly controlling diapause and regeneration.

obligatory Essential: a necessary mode of life, unable to exist in any other role, *cf.* facultative.

oesophagus Regions of the gut between the pharynx and (in earthworms) the intestine; in many earthworms families (*not* Lumbricidae) developed locally to form one or more gizzards while calciferous glands are present in most terrestrial genera.

omnivorous Non-selective feeder consuming a mixed diet of plant and animal material.

oöcyte A diploid cell that produces haploid eggs (ova) by meiotic division.

oöphore Egg case or capsule.

osmoregulation The control of the osmotic pressure of solutes in the intercellular liquids of animals, mostly associated with the removal of waste products and/or water by the excretory organs.

oviduct In earthworms: the duct with a fimbriated funnel at its ental end that conveys mature ova from the region of the ovary to the exterior through the female pore on segment *xiv*.

ovum (*pl.* **ova**) An unfertilized egg; the female gamete with a haploid number of chromosomes.

palaearctic region A zoogeographical region comprising Europe and northern Asia including Japan, the Middle and Near East and areas along the southern coast of the Mediterranean Sea.

parasitization Invasion by an organism metabolically dependent upon the host for the completion of its life cycle; typically detrimental to the host, *cf.* commensalism, symbiosis.

parthenogenesis The development of an individual from a female gamete (*ovum*) without fertilization by a male gamete (*spermatozöon*).

pathological Produced by disease or infestations of parasites.

penial seta (*pl.* **penial setae**) Supernumerary setae that facilitate the passage of sperm during copulation, occurring near the male or prostatic pores especially in the superfamily Megascolecoidea; usually long and ornamented perhaps numerous in (paired) bundles.

peregrine *See* allochthonous.

perichaetine Condition with numerous setae around the equator of each setigerous segment; more than four pairs present, possibly up to two hundred setae around a single segment, *cf.* lumbricine.

periproct The last segment of the body bearing the anus.

peristomium The first segment of the body surrounding the mouth and dorsally carrying the prostomium; without setae.

peritoneum The membrane lining the coelom, containing and often supporting the principal organs; derived from the embryonic mesoderm.

pF The water potential of a soil; a measure of the total capillary pull (suction force) with which water is held by soil and indicating the relative availability of the water to plants and soil animals; logarithm of the height in centimeters of a column of water corresponding to the free-energy difference between free water and that held by the soil. Most plants tend to wilt at pF 4·4 but water is usually freely available at pF 2·0 (field capacity).

pH Acidity on a scale from 0 (acid) through (neutral) to 14 (alkaline): a negative logarithm of the hydrogen ion (H^+) concentration.

pharynx The fore part of the alimentary canal between the mouth and the oesophagus containing the buccal cavity.

pleisiomorphic Primitive, ancestral character, *cf.* apomorphic.

Pleistocene A geological epoch of the Quaternary period (*ca.* 1.6–0.01 million years BP).

poikilothermic An animal with a body temperature varying with that of the surroundings and often modified by radiant heat from the sun or cooling by evaporation, *cf.* homoiothermic.

polymorphic A species having several genetically determined morphological phases.

polyploid Having more than two sets of homologous chromosomes, *cf.* diploid, haploid.

porophore Papilla bearing a pore.

155

proandry In earthworms: the presence of a single pair of testes in segment x, *cf.* holandry, metandry.

prolobous Characterising a prostomium demarcated from and without a tongue into the peristomium.

prostate A paired gland in megascolecoid earthworms producing a fluid for the transport and (?) nourishment of sperm during copulation; either associated with the vas deferens or opening with a separate duct discharging through or nearby a male pore.

prostomium Pre-segmental, dorsal protuberance of the peristomium, infrequently (exotic species) developed into a proboscis; used for probing and in browsing species for grasping leaves, blades of grass etc.; tactile, believed to be highly chemosensory.

proximal Basal, near to the point of attachment, *cf.* distal.

pseudoheart *See* lateral commissure.

Quaternary A geological period of the Cenozoic (*ca.* 1.6 million years BP to present), comprising the Pleistocene and the Holocene epochs.

quiescence A temporary state of inactivity caused by adverse environmental conditions and terminated as soon as conditions become favourable *cf.* diapause.

r-**selected species** A species characteristic of variable or unpredictable environments; typically with rapid development, high innate capacity for increase (r), early reproduction, small body size and semelparity; opportunistic species that disperse rapidly and are effective early colonizers, *cf.* K-selected species.

regeneration Regrowth of an organ or part of the body that has been injured or lost.

rhizophagous Root feeding.

saddle-shaped Clitellum incomplete ventrally, *cf.* annular.

secondary sexual characters Structures other than the gonads and gametes that develop with sexual maturity.

segment A single body compartment forming a complete unit usually separated from other such adjacent (anterior and posterior) units by septa; each unit has setae, muscles, nerves, ganglia, blood vessels, nephridia etc. (In earthworms the various elements of the digestive system and the reproductive organs are restricted to only certain segments.) Believed to be the evolutionary relic of a single individual that with others once formed a colonial organism, *see* metamere.

self fertilization The union of the male and female gametes produced by the same individual.

seminal vesicle Pouch formed in a (usually posterior) septum of a testicular segment where the spermatogenia/spermatocytes undergo the later stages of spermatogenesis and are stored until required during copulation.

septum (*pl.* **septa**) Two layers of peritoneal cells enclosing muscle fibres, connective tissue and blood vessels separating adjacent segments; usually delicate but sometimes thickened between anterior segments.

seta (*pl.* **setae**) Bristle of chitin, the product of a single ectodermal cell: each seta has its own musculature and is used mainly in locomotion, for gripping (in browsing species) the entrance to a burrow or when it is enlarged for holding another individual during copulation (genital seta); in some megascolecoid genera additional setae are present by the male pores, *see* penial seta. From *saeta* (Latin) = bristle.

setigerous Bearing setae.

sperm reservoir In the subfamily Eudrilinae, a small testis sac investing a testis, continuous entally with the adjacent seminal vesicle and ectally with its vas deferens.

spermatheca (*pl.* **spermathecae**) Flask-like invagination of the body wall for the reception and storage of sperm from a partner during copulation. The ectal region is frequently slender, the *spermathecal duct*; whereas the ental region is dilated to form a conical to dome-like *ampulla*.

spermatogonium (*pl.* **spermatogonia**) A cell produced by the testis which by repeated mitotic division develops into a spermatocyte then in turn, divides by meiotic division to produce the male gametes.

spermatophore A packet of spermatozoa enclosed in membranous sac usually for transfer to another individual especially in species lacking spermathecae.

spermatozoön (*pl.* **spermatozoa**) Produced by a spermatocyte, the male gamete with the haploid number of chromosomes.

stenohaline Unable to tolerate variations in osmotic pressure, i.e. either strictly freshwater or strictly marine, *cf.* euryhaline.

sub-neural vessel A longitudinal blood vessel situated below the ventral nerve cord in the intestinal region, connected to the dorsal vessel by the segmental commissural vessels.

symbiosis The living together of two organisms, commonly an association that is mutually beneficial.

tanylobous Characterising a prostomium with a tongue that passes back through the peristomium to furrow 1/2, *cf.* epilobous, prolobous.

taxon A discrete group of organisms with a unique name, i.e. species, genus, family etc.

testis sac An investment of the testis by a membranous sac that is continuous with the seminal vesicle and contains the funnel to the vas deferens.

Tethys Sea The epicontinental sea separating Laurasia from Gondwana following the break up of Pangaea in the Mesozoic.

tubercula pubertatis (*sing.* **tuberculum pubertatis**) The tubercles of puberty; paired papillose or ridge-like glandular tumescences forming discrete genital pads in the clitellar region of mature adults practising copulation. (*Note.* tubercul*a*, nominative plural of tubercul*um*; pubert*atis*, genitive singular of pubert*as*.)

tumescence A raised, swollen, glandular area.

Turgai Straits A late Mesozoic epicontinental sea passing north-south between what is now Europe and Asia, from mid-Jurassic times (150 Mya) to early Palaeocene and most of the Eocene.

typhlosole A dorsal infolding of the anterior to mid-intestine of an earthworm giving an increased surface area for digestion and the absorption of nutrients.

uniparental Production of young by a single adult either by self-fertilization or by parthenogenesis.

vascular system The arterial and venous vessels forming a network for the transport of blood.

vas deferens (*pl.* **vasa deferentia**) Duct conveying sperm from the male funnel to the male pore.

ventral (blood) vessel or **trunk** The large, longitudinal blood vessel below the gut, anteriorly receiving blood from the lateral commissures and carrying it posteriorly to the body.

vermiculture Breeding and culturing worms.

zygolobous A prostomium that is not in any way demarcated from the peristomium.

Roman numerals

1	*i*	7	*vii*	20	*xx*	41	*xli*
2	*ii*	8	*viii*	21	*xxi*	49	*il*
3	*iii*	9	*ix*	29	*xxix*	50	*l*
4	*iv*	10	*x*	30	*xxx*	100	*c*
5	*v*	11	*xi*	39	*ixl*	500	*d*
6	*vi*	19	*xix*	40	*xl*	1000	*m*

References

André, F. 1963. Contribution à l'analyse expérimentale de la reproduction des Lombriciens. *Bull. biol. Fr. Belg.* **97**(1), 1–101.

Anon. 1975. Earthworms. *Zoology Leaflet* **9**, 1–5. London: British Museum (Natural History).

Appelhof, M. 1980. Vermicomposting on a household scale. In *Soil biology as related to land use practices. Proceedings of the VII International Colloquium of Soil Zoology*, ed., Dindal, D. L. pp. 157–160. Washington: Environmental Protection Agency.

Appelhof, M. (Editor) 1981. *Workshop on the role of earthworms in the stabilization of organic residues.* Volume 1 (Proceedings), 315 pp. Kalamazoo, Michigan: Beech Leaf Press.

Baird, W. 1869a. Description of a new species of earthworm (*Megascolex diffringens*) found in North Wales. *Proc. zool. Soc. Lond. 1869*, 40–43.

Baird, W. 1869b. Additional remarks on the *Megascolex diffringens*. *Proc. zool. Soc. Lond. 1869*, 387–389.

Barrett. T. J. 1949. *Harnessing the earthworm.* 166 pp. London: Faber and Faber.

Beddard, F. E. 1890. Exhibition of and remarks upon, some living specimens of oriental earthworms, found in a greenhouse in Scotland. *Proc. zool. Soc. Lond. 1890*, 94.

Beddard, F. E. 1891. On the structure of two new genera of earthworms belonging to the Eudrilidae and some remarks on *Nematodrilus*. *Q. Jl microsc. Sci.* **32**, 235–278.

Beddard, F. E. 1892a. On some species of the genus *Perichaeta* (sensu stricta). *Proc. zool. Soc. Lond. 1892*, 153–172.

Beddard, F. E. 1892b. On a new genus of Oligochaeta comprising five new species belonging to the family Ocnerodrilidae, *Ann. Mag. nat. Hist.* Ser. 6 **10**, 74–97.

Beddard, F. E. 1892c. On some Perichaetidae from Japan. *Zool. Jahr* (Syst.) **6**, 755–766.

Beddard, F. E. 1893a. Two new genera and some new species of earthworms. *Q. Jl microsc. Sci.* **34**, 243–278.

Beddard, F. E. 1893b. On some new species of earthworms from various parts of the world. *Proc. zool. Soc. Lond. 1892*, 666–706.

Beddard, F. E. 1894. On two new genera, comprising three new species of earthworms, from western tropical Africa. *Proc. zool. Soc. Lond. 1894*, 379–390.

Beddard, F. E. 1899. A note on phosphorescent earthworms. *Nature* (No. 1542) **60**, 52.

Beddard, F. E. 1901. Contributions to the knowledge of the structure and systematic arrangement of earthworms. *Proc. zool. Soc. Lond. 1901*, 187–206.

Beddard, F. E. 1906. Annelida. Oligochaeta. *Addit. Ser. Kew* **5**, 66–67.

Benham, W. B. 1892. A new English genus of aquatic Oligochaeta (*Sparganophilus*) belonging to the family Rhinodrilidae. *Q. Jl microsc. Sci.* **34**, 155–179.

Bouché, M. B. 1969. *Ailoscolex lacteospumosus* n.gen., n.sp.. Un ver de terre aux caractères morphologiques et biologiques remarquables (Oligochaeta, Ailoscolecidae, nov. fam.). *Revue Écol. Biol. Sol* **6** (4), 525–531.

Bouché, M. B. 1970. Remarques sur quelques Lumbricina de France et consequences de la découverte des nouveaux taxons Vignysinae (subfam. nov.) et Diporodrilidae (fam. nov.). *Pedobiologia* **10**, 246–256.

Bouché, M. B. 1972. Lombriciens de France. Écologie et systématique. *Annls Zool. Écol. anim.* (Num. spec.) **72–2**, 1–671.

Bouché, M. B. 1975. La reproduction de *Spermophorodrilus albanianus* nov. gen., nov. sp. (Lumbricidae), explique-t-elle la fonction des spermatophores? *Zool. Jb.* (Syst.) **102**, 1–11.

Bouché, M. B. 1976. Contribution à la stabilisation de la nomenclature des Lumbricidae, Oligochaeta, I. Synonymies et homonymies d'espèces du Bassin Parisien. *Bull. Mus. natn. Hist nat.* (Zool.) (Ser. 3, No. 354) **247**, 81–88.

Bouché, M. B. 1980. L'interprétation morphologique des lombriciens: un commentaire de l'evaluation numerique de R. W. Sims. *Pedobiologia* **20**, 227–229.

Bouché, M. B. 1983. The establishment of earthworm communities, In *Earthworm ecology from Darwin to vermiculture*, ed. Satchell, J. E., 431–448. London: Chapman and Hall.

Brinkhurst, R. O. 1982a. British and other marine and estuarine oligochaetes. *Synopses of the British Fauna* (New Series) **21** 127 pp. Linnean Society of London, Estuarine and Brackish Water Sciences Association and Cambridge University Press.

Brinkhurst, R. O. 1982b. Evolution in the Annelida. *Can. J. Zool.* **60**(5), 1043–1059.

Černosvitov, L. 1942. Revision of Friend's types and descriptions of British Oligochaeta. *Proc. zool. Soc. Lond.* Ser. B **111**, 237–280.

Černosvitov, L. and Evans, A. C. 1947. Lumbricidae (Annelida). With a key to the common species. *Synopses of the British Fauna.* **6**, 36 pp. London: The Linnean Society of London.

Clark, R. B. 1981. Locomotion and phylogeny of the Metazoa. *Boll. Zool.* **48**(1), 11–28.

Claus, C. F. W. 1880. *Grundzüge der Zoologie* 4th edn **1**, 821 pp. Marburg: Elwert.

Cognetti, L. 1901. Gli oligocheti della Sardegna. *Boll. Mus. zool. Anat. Comp. Torino* **16** (404), 1–26.

Cognetti, L. 1904. Lombricidi dei Pirenei. *Boll. Mus. zool. Anat. comp. Torino* **19**(476), 1–14.

Cotton, D. C. F. 1978. A revision of the Irish earthworms (Oligochaeta: Lumbricidae) with the addition of two species. *Ir. Nat. J.* **19**(8), 257–260.

Cotton, D. C. F. 1979. *Aporrectodea icterica* (Savigny, 1826); an earthworm new to Ireland. *Ir. Nat. J.* **19**(11), 387–388.

Cotton, D. C. F. and Curry, J. P. 1980a. The effects of cattle and pig slurry fertilizers on earthworms (Oligochaeta, Lumbricidae) in grassland managed for silage production. *Pedobiologia* **20**, 181–188.

Cotton, D. C. F. and Curry, J. P. 1980b. The response of earthworm populations (Oligochaeta, Lumbricidae) to high applications of pig slurry. *Pedobiologia* **20**, 189–196.

Cuendet, G. 1979. Etude du comportement alimentaire de la mouette rieuse, *Larus ridibundus*, et de son influence sur les peuplements de lombrics. *Nos Oiseaux* **35** (4), 170–172.

Cuendet, G. 1984. A comparative study of the earthworm population of four different woodland types in Whytham woods, Oxford. *Pedobiologia* **26**, 421–439.

Darwin, C. 1881. *The formation of vegetable mould through the action of worms with observations on their habits.* 328 pp. London: John Murray.

160

Davey, S. P. 1963. Effects of chemicals on earthworms: a review of the literature. *Spec. scient. Rep. U.S. Fish Wildl. Serv.* **74**, 1.

Dobson, R. M. and Satchell, J. E. 1956. *Eophila oculata* at Verulamium: a Roman earthworm population? *Nature, London* **177**, 796–797.

Duboscq, O. 1902. *Alma zebanguii* n.sp. et les Alminae oligochètes de la famille des Glossoscolecidae Mich. *Archs Zool. exp. gen.* Notes 3 **10**(7), xcvii–cvi.

Dugès, A. 1828. Recherches sur la circulation, la respiration et la reproduction des Annélides abranches sétigères. *Ann. Sci. nat.* **15**, 285–337.

Dugès, A. 1837. Nouvelles observations sur la zoologie et l'anatomie des Annélides abranches sétigères. *Annls Sci. nat.* (Zool.) **8**, 15–35.

Easton, E. G. 1979. A revision of the 'acaecate' earthworms of the *Pheretima* group (Megascolecidae: Oligochaeta): *Archipheretima, Metapheretima, Planapheretima, Pleinogaster* and *Polypheretima. Bull. Br. Mus. nat. Hist.* (Zool.) **35**(1), 1–126.

Easton, E. G. 1983. A guide to the valid names of Lumbricidae (Oligochaeta). In *Earthworm ecology from Darwin to vermiculture*, ed. Satchell, J. E., pp. 475–487. London: Chapman and Hall

Easton, E. G. 1986. The allochthonous perichaetine earthworms of the world. *Bull. Br. Mus. nat. Hist* (Zool.): (in press).

Edwards, C. A. 1979. Tests to assess the effects of pesticides on beneficial soil organisms. In *Tests for the ecological effects of chemicals*, pp. 249–253. Berlin: Erich Schmidt.

Edwards, C. A. 1980. Interaction between agricultural practice and earthworms. In *Soil biology as related to land use practices. Proceedings of the VII International Colloquium of soil zoology*, ed. Dindal, D. L. pp. 3–12. Washington: Environmental Protection Agency.

Edwards, C. A. 1983. Earthworm ecology in cultivated soils. In *Earthworm ecology from Darwin to vermiculture*, ed. Satchell, J. E., 123–137. London: Chapman and Hall.

Edwards, C. A. and Lofty, J. R. 1975. The influence of cultivations on soil animal populations. In *Progress in soil zoology. Proceedings of the V International Colloquium of Soil Zoology*, ed. Vaněk, J. pp. 399–408. Prague: Academia.

Edwards, C. A. and Lofty, J. R. 1977. *Biology of earthworms* 2nd edn, 333 pp. London: Chapman and Hall.

Eisen, G. 1873. Om Skandinaviens Lumbricider. *Ofvers. K. Vetensk Akad. Förh. Stockh.* **30**(8), 43–56.

Eisen, G. 1874. Bidrag till Kannedomen om New Englands och Canadas Lumbricider. *Ofvers. K. Vetensk Akad. Förh. Stockh.* **31**(2), 1–11.

Evans, A. C. 1946. A new species of earthworm of the genus *Allolobophora. Ann. Mag. nat. Hist.* Ser. 11, **14**, 98–101.

Evans, A. C. and Guild, W. J. McL. 1948. On the cocoons of some British Lumbricidae. *Ann. Mag. nat. Hist.* ser. 11 **14**(1947), 714–719.

Fender, W. M. 1982. *Dendrobaena attemsi* in an American greenhouse, with notes on its morphology and systematic position. *Megadrilogica* **4**(1–2), 8–11.

Friend, H. 1891. Earthworms of the north of England. *Naturalist, Hull* **16**, 13–15.

Friend H. 1892. On a new species of earthworm. *Proc. R. Irish Acad.* Ser. 3 **11**, 402–410.

Friend, H. 1904. New garden worms. *Gardeners' Chronicle* Ser. 3 **35**, 161.

Friend, H. 1909. New garden worms. *Gardeners' Chronicle* Ser. 3 **46**, 243 (October 9).

Friend, H. 1910. XIV. Additions to the wild fauna and flora of the Royal Botanic Gardens, Kew: XI. *Bull. Misc. Inf. R. bot. Gdns, Kew* **3**, 79–82.

161

Friend, H. 1911a. The distribution of British annelids. *Zoologist* Ser. 4, **15**, 142–146, 184–191.

Friend, H. 1911b. New annelids. *Zoologist* Ser. 4, **15**, 273–275.

Friend, H. 1913a. Annelid hunting in Notts. *Rep. Trans. Notts Nat. Soc.* **61**, 20–38.

Friend, H. 1913b. Some Jersey Oligochaets. *Zoologist* Ser. 4, **17**, 456–464.

Friend, H. 1916. Alien oligochaets in England. *J. Roy. microsc. Soc. 1916,* 147–157, 262–271.

Friend, H. 1921. Two new aquatic annelids. *Ann. Mag. nat. Hist.* Ser. 9, **7**, 137–141.

Friend, H. 1924. *The story of British annelids,* 288 pp. London: Sharp.

Gates, G. E. 1956. Notes on American earthworms of the family Lumbricidae. *Bull. Mus. comp. Zool. Harv.* **115**(1), 1–46.

Gates, G. E. 1957. Contributions to a revision of the earthworm family Lumbricidae. I, *Allolobophora limicola. Breviora* **81**, 1–14.

Gates, G. E. 1963. Miscellanea Megadrilogica VII. Greenhouse earthworms. *Proc. biol. Soc. Wash.* **79**, 9–17.

Gates, G. E. 1968a. Contributions to a revision of the Lumbricidae. III, *Dendrobaena hortensis* (Michaelsen, 1890). *Breviora* **300**, 1–12.

Gates, G. E. 1968b. What is *Lumbricus eiseni* Levinsen, 1884 (Lumbricidae, Oligochaeta)? *Breviora* **299**, 1–9.

Gates, G. E. 1969. Contributions to a revision of the earthworm family Lumbricidae. V, *Eisenia zebra* Michaelsen, 1902. *Proc. biol. Soc. Wash.* **82**, 453–460.

Gates, G. E. 1970. Miscellanea Megadrilogica VIII. *Megadrilogica* **1**(2), 1–14.

Gates, G. E. 1972a. Burmese earthworms, an introduction to the systematics and biology of megadrile oligochaetes with special reference to southeast Asia. *Trans. Am. phil. Soc.* **62**(7), 1–326.

Gates, G. E. 1972b. Contributions to North American earthworms No. 3. Toward a revision of the earthworm family Lumbricidae IV. The *trapezoides* species group. *Bull. Tall Timbers res. Stn* **12**, 1–146.

Gates, G. E. 1973. Contributions to North American earthworms (Annelida) No. 8. The earthworm genus *Octolasion* in America. *Bull. Tall Timbers res. Stn* **14**, 29–50.

Gates, G. E. 1974a. On a new species of earthworm in a southern portion of the United States. *Bull. Tall Timbers res. Stn* **15**, 1–13.

Gates, G. E. 1974b. Contributions on North American earthworms (Annelida), No. 10. Contributions to a revision of the Lumbricidae X. *Dendrobaena octaedra* (Savigny, 1826) with special reference to the importance of its parthenogenetic polymorphism for the classification of earthworms. *Bull. Tall Timbers res. Stn* **15**, 15–57.

Gates, G. E. 1974c. Contributions on North American earthworms (Annelida) No. 12. Contributions to a revision of the family Lumbricidae XI. *Eisenia rosea* (Savigny, 1826). *Bull. Tall Timbers res. Stn* **16**, 9–30.

Gates G. E. 1975a. Contributions to a revision of the earthworm family Lumbricidae, XII. *Enterion mammale* Savigny, 1826 and its position in the family. *Megadrilogica* **2**(1), 1–8.

Gates, G. E. 1975b. Contributions to a revision of the earthworm family Lumbricidae XV. On some other species of *Eisenia. Megadrilogica* **2**(5), 1–7.

Gates, G. E. 1975c. Contributions to a revision of the earthworm family Lumbricidae, XVII. *Allolobophora minuscula* Rosa, 1906 and *Enterion pygmaeum* Savigny, 1826. *Megadrilogica* **2**(6), 7–8.

Gates, G. E. 1976. Contributions to a revision of the earthworm family Lumbricidae, XIX. On the genus of the earthworm *Enterion roseum* Savigny, 1826. *Megadrilogica* **2**(12), 4.

Gates, G. E. 1977a. On the correct generic name for some west coast native earthworms, with aids for a study of the genus. *Megadrilogica* 3(4), 54–60.

Gates, G. E. 1977b. Contributions to a revision of the earthworm family Lumbricidae, XX. The genus *Eiseniella* in North America. *Megadrilogica* 3(5), 71–79.

Gates, G. E. 1978a. The earthworm genus *Lumbricus* in North America. *Megadrilogica* 3(6), 81–116.

Gates, G. E. 1978b. Contributions to a revision of the earthworm family Lumbricidae, XXII. The genus *Eisenia* in North America. *Megadrilogica* 3(8), 131–147.

Gates, G. E. 1979. Contributions to a revision of the earthworm family Lumbricidae, XXIII. The genus *Dendrodrilus* Omodeo, 1956 in North America. *Megadrilogica* 3(9), 151–162.

Gates, G. E. 1980. Contributions to a revision of the earthworm family Lumbricidae, XXV. The genus *Allolobophora* Eisen, 1874 in North America. *Megadrilogica* 3(11), 177–184.

Gates, G. E. 1982. Farewell to North America megadriles. *Megadrilogica* 4(1–2), 12–77.

Gerard, B. M. 1964. Lumbricidae (Annelida) with keys and descriptions. (Second edition) *Synopses of the British Fauna.* 6, 58 pp. London: The Linnean Society of London.

Gerard, B. M. 1967. Factors affecting earthworms in pastures. *J. Anim. Ecol.* 36, 235–252.

Gerard, B. M. and Hay, R. K. M. 1979. The effect on earthworms of ploughing, tined cultivation, direct drilling and nitrogen in a barley monoculture system. *J. agric. Sci.* 93(1), 147–155.

Godman, A. and Payne, E. M. F. 1979. *Longman dictionary of scientific usage.* 684 pp. London: Longman.

Graff, O. 1953. Die Regenwürmer Deutschlands. *Schrift Forsch. land Braunschweig-Volk,* 7, 1–81.

Graff, O. and Makeschin, F. 1979. Der Einfluss der Fauna auf die Stoffverlagerung sowie die Homogenität und die Durchlässikeit von Boden. *Z. Pflanzenernaehr. Bodenkd.* 42, 476–491.

Grube, E. 1879. An account of the petrological, botanical and zoological collections made in Kerguelen's Land and Rodriguez during the *Transit of Venus Expedition* carried out by order of Her Majesty's Government in the years 1874–75. Annelida. *Phil. Trans. R. Soc.* 168, 554–556.

Guerro, R. D. 1983. Studies on the culture and use of *Perionyx excavatus* as a protein resource in the Philippines. In *Earthworm ecology from Darwin to vermiculture,* ed. Satchell, J. E., 309–313. London: Chapman and Hall.

Hartenstein, R., Neuhauser, E. F. & Easton, E. G. 1980. Growth and fecundity of F_2 *Eisenia foetida* derived from F_1s, both reared in isolation from birth. *Megadrilogica* 3(11), 185–187.

Hoffmeister, W. 1843. Beitrag zur Kenntniss deutscher Landanneliden. *Arch. Naturgesch.* 9, 183–198.

Hoffmeister, W. 1845. *Die bis jetzt bekannten Arten aus der Familie der Regenwürmer. Als Grundlage zu einer Monographie dieser Famillie.* 43 pp. Braunschweig.

Horst, R. 1883. New species of the genus *Megascolex* Templeton (*Perichaeta* Schmarda) in the collections of the Leyden Museum. *Notes Leyden Mus.* 5, 182–196.

Jaenike, J. 1982. '*Eisenia foetida*' is two species. *Megadrilogica* 4(1–2), 6–8.

Jamieson, B. G. M. 1971. In *Aquatic Oligochaeta of the World,* ed. Brinkhurst R. O. & Jamieson, B. G. M. 860 pp. Edinburgh: Oliver & Boyd.

Jamieson, B. G. M. 1973. Earthworms (Megascolecidae: Oligochaeta) from Mount Kosciusko, Australia. *Rec. Aust. Mus.* **28**(11), 215–251.

Jamieson, B. G. M. 1974. The indigenous earthworms (Megascolecidae: Oligochaeta) of Tasmania. *Bull. Br. Mus. nat. Hist.* (Zool.) **26**(4), 204–328.

Jamieson, B. G. M. and Wampler, J. E. 1979. Bioluminescent Australian earthworms II. Taxonomy and preliminary report of bioluminescence in the genera *Spenceriella, Fletcherodrilus* and *Pontodrilus* (Megascolidae, Oligochaeta). *Aust. J. Zool.* **27**, 637–669.

Kinberg, J. G. H. 1867. Annulata nova. *Ofvers. K. Vetensk Akad. Förh. Stockh.* **23**, 97–103, 356–357.

Lakhani, K. H. and Satchell, J. E. 1970. Production by *Lumbricus terrestris* (L.). *J. Anim. Ecol.* **39**, 473–492.

Laverack, M. S. 1963. *The physiology of earthworms.* 206 pp. Oxford: Pergamon Press.

Leftwich, A. W. 1967. *A dictionary of zoology.* 2nd edn, 319 pp. London: Constable, and, Princeton, New Jersey: van Nostrand.

Levinsen, G. M. R. 1884. Systematisk-geografisk. Oversigt over de nordiske Annulata, Gephyrea, Chaetognathi, og Balanoglossi. *Vidensk. Meddr. dansk naturh. Foren. 1883,* 92–350.

Lincoln, R. J., Boxshall, G. A. and Clark, P. F. 1982. *A dictionary of ecology, evolution and systematics.* 298 pp. Cambridge: Cambridge University Press.

Lincoln, R. J. and Sheals, J. G. 1979. *Invertebrate animals: collection* and *preservation.* 150 pp. London: British Museum (Natural History).

Linnaeus, C. 1758. *Systema naturae . . .* **1**, 824 pp. (10th edn). Holmiae: Salvii.

Macdonald, D. W. 1983. Predation on earthworms by terrestrial vertebrates. In *Earthworm ecology from Darwin to Vermiculture,* ed. Satchell, J. E., 393–444. London: Chapman & Hall.

Macfadyen, A. 1963. The contribution of the microfauna to soil metabolism. In *Soil Organisms,* eds Doeksen, J. and Drift, J. van der, pp. 3–17. Amsterdam: North Holland Publishing Company.

Macfadyen, A. 1975. ed. *Advances in ecological research* **8**, 418 pp. London & New York: Academic Press.

McKey-Fender, D. and Fender, W. M. 1982. *Arctiostrotus* (gen. nov.). Part I. The identity of *Plutellus perrieri* Benham, 1892 and its distribution in relation to glacial refugia. *Megadrilogica* **4**(3), 81–85.

McMahon, M. L. 1976. Preliminary notes on a new megadrile species, genus and family from the southeastern United States. *Megadrilogica* **2**(11), 6–8.

Malm, A. W. 1877. Om Daggmaskar, Lumbricina. *Öfvers. Sällsk. Hort. Vänn. Göteborgs Förh. 1877,* 34–47.

Mazantseva, G. P. 1982. Growth patterns in the earthworm *Nicodrilus caliginosus* (Oligochaeta: Lumbricidae) during the first year of life. *Pedobiologia* **23**, 272–276.

Michaelsen, W. 1890. Die Lumbriciden Norddeutschlands. *Jb. hamb. wiss. Anst.* **7**, 1–19.

Michaelsen, W. 1891. Oligochaeten des Naturhistorischen Museum in Hamburg, IV. *Jb. hamb. wiss. Anst.* **8**, 3–42.

Michaelsen, W. 1899. Revison der Kinbergschen Oligochäten-Typen. *Ofvers. K. Vetensk Akad. Förh. Stockh.* **56**, 413–448.

Michaelsen, W. 1900. Oligochaeta. *Tierreich* **10**, 1–575.

Michaelsen, W. 1902. Neue Oligochäten und neue Fundorte alt-bekannter. *Jb. hamb. wiss. Anst.* **19**(2), 1–54.

164

Michaelsen, W. 1903. *Die geographische Verbreitung der Oligochaeten.* 186 pp. Berlin: Friedländer.

Michaelsen, W. 1935. Oligochaeta from Christmas Island, south of Java. *Ann. Mag. nat. Hist.* ser. 10 **15**, 100–108.

Miles, H. B. 1963. Soil Protozoa and earthworm nutrition. *Soil Science* **95**(6), 407–409.

Minnich, J. 1977. *The earthworm book.* 372 pp. Emmaus, Pennsylvania: Rodale Press.

Moment, G. B. 1979. Growth, posterior regeneration and segment number in *Eisenia fetida. Megadrilogica* **3**(10), 167–175.

Muldal, S. 1952. A new species of earthworm of the genus *Allolobophora. Proc. zool. Soc. Lond.* **122**, 463–465.

Müller, F. 1857. *Lumbricus corethrurus,* Bürstenschwanz. *Arch. Naturgesch.* **23**, 113–116.

Murchie, W. R. 1955. A contribution on the natural history of *Allolobophora minima* Muldal (Lumbricidae). *Ohio J. Sci.* **55**, 241–244.

Murchie, W. R. 1959. Redescription of *Allolobophora muldali* Omodeo, 1956 (Lumbricidae: Oligochaeta). *Ohio J. Sci.* **59**(6), 329–332.

Nakamura, Y. 1982. Colonization by earthworms of Niimi waste water treatment trenches. *Pedobiologia* **23**, 399–402.

Øien, N. and Stenersen, J. 1984. Enterases of earthworms—III. Electrophoresis reveals that *Eisenia fetida* (Savigny) is two species. *Comp. Biochem. Physiol.* **78C**(2), 277–282.

Omodeo, P. 1952. Materiali zoologici raccolti dal Dr. Marcuzzi sulle Alpi Dolomitiche. *Archo. zool. ital.* **37**, 29–59.

Omodeo, P. 1956. Contributo alla revisione dei Lumbricidae. *Archo. zool. ital.* **41**, 129–212.

Örley, L. 1881. A magyarorszagi Oligochaeták Faunája; Terricolae (Reudszertani rész). *Math. Term. tud. Közlem* **16**, 561–611.

Örley, L. 1885. A palaearktikus övben élö Terricoláknak reviziója és elterjedése. *Értek. Term. tud. Kor.* **15**, 1–34.

Perel, T. S. 1976. A critical analysis of the Lumbricidae genera system (with key to the USSR fauna genera). *Rev. Écol. Biol. Sol* **13**(4), 635–643.

Perel, T. S. 1979. [*Range and regularities in the distribution of earthworms of the USSR fauna.*] 268 pp. Moscow: Nauka [Russian]

Perel, T. S. 1982. [Geographical peculiarities of reproduction of the earthworms of the family Lumbricidae (Oligochaeta).] *Zool. Z.* **43**(5), 649–658. [Russian: English summary]

Perrier, E. 1872. Recherches pour servir a l'histoire des Lombriciens terrestres. *Nouv. Archs Mus. Hist. nat. Paris* **8**, 5–198.

Pickford, G. E. 1926. On a new species of earthworm belonging to the subgenus *Bimastus* from Wicken Fen. *Ann. Mag. nat. Hist.* Ser. 9, **17**, 96–98.

Piearce, T. G. 1983. Functional morphology of lumbricid earthworms with special reference to locomotion. *J. nat. Hist.* **17**, 95–111.

Plisko, J. D. 1961. Analizn materialów dzdzownic (Lumbricidae) zmagazynowanych przez kreta (*Talpa europea* L.). *Fragm. faun.* **9**(7), 61–73.

Pop, V. 1941. Zur Phylogenie und Systematik der Lumbriciden. *Zool. Jb.* (Syst.) **74**, 487–522.

Pop, V. 1948 Lumbricidele din România. *Anal. Acad. rom.* (Geol. Geogr. Biol.) Ser. A, **1**(9), 1–124.

Rafinesque-Schmaltz, C. S. 1815. *Analyse de la nature ou tableau de l'univers et des corps organises . . .*, 224 pp. Palermo.

Reinecke, A. J. and Kriel, J. R. 1981. The influence of constant and diurnally fluctuating temperatures on cocoon production, hatching time and number of hatchlings of *Eisenia fetida* (Lumbricidae, Oligochaeta). In *Workshop on the role of earthworms in the stabilization of organic residues*. (Proceedings) ed. Appelhof, M. **1**, 166–177. Kalamazoo, Michigan: Beech Leaf Press.

Reynolds, J. W. 1976. *Aporrectodea icterica* (Savigny, 1826) une espèce Européen de vers de terre récement découverte en Amérique du nord. *Megadrilogica* **2**(12), 3–4.

Reynolds, J. W. 1977. The earthworms (Lumbricidae and Sperganophilidae) of Ontario. *Life Sci. misc. Publs R. Ont. Mus. 1977*, 1–141.

Reynolds, J. W. 1980. The earthworm family Sparganophilidae (Annelida, Oligochaeta) in North America. *Megadrilogica* **3**(12), 189–204.

Rosa, D. 1884. *Lumbricidi del Piemonte*. 54 pp. Torino.

Rosa, D. 1886. Noti sui Lombrici del Veneto. *Boll. Musei Zool. Anat. Comp. R. Univ. Torino* **1**(2), 1–2. [Abstract of: *Atti R. Ist. veneto Sci.* Ser. 6 **4**, 674 (1886).]

Rosa, D. 1891. Die exotischen Terricolen des k.k. naturhistorischen Hofmuseums. *Annln naturh. Mus. Wien* **6**, 379–406.

Rosa, D. 1893. Revisione dei Lubricidi. *Memorie Accad. Sci. Torino* Ser. 2, **43**, 399–476.

Rosa, D. 1906. *L'Allolobophora minuscula* n.sp. *Atti. Soc. Nat. Mat. Moderna* Ser. 47 (1905), 38–39.

Sabine, J. R. 1983. Earthworms as a source of food and drugs. In *Earthworm ecology from Darwin to vermiculture*, ed. Satchell, J. E., 285–296. London: Chapman & Hall.

Satchell, J. E. 1955. Some aspects of earthworm ecology. In *Soil Zoology: Proceedings of the University of Nottingham Second Easter School in Agricultural Science*, ed., Kevan, D. K. McE. pp. 180–201. London: Butterworths.

Satchell, J. E. 1958. Earthworm biology and soil fertility. *Soils and Fertilizers* **21**, 209–219.

Satchell, J. E. 1967. Colour dimorphism in *Allolobophora chlorotica* Sav. (Lumbricidae). *J. anim. Ecol.* **36**, 623–630.

Satchell, J. E. 1980. *r* worms and *K* worms: a basis for classifying lumbricid earthworm strategies. In *Soil biology as related to land use practices. Proceedings of the VII International Colloquim of Soil Zoology*, ed. Dindal, D. L. pp. 848–864. Washington: Environmental Protection Agency.

Satchell, J. E. 1981. Earthworm evolution: Pangaea to production prototype. In *Workshop on the role of earthworms in the stabilization of organic residues*. (Proceedings) ed. Appelhof, M. **1**, 3–35. Kalamazoo, Michigan: Beech Leaf Press.

Satchell, J. E. 1983. Earthworms and microflora. In *Earthworm ecology from Darwin to vermiculture*, ed. Satchell, J. E., pp. 351–363. London: Chapman and Hall.

Saussey, M. 1966. Contribution à l'étude des phénomènes de diapause et de régénération caudale chez *Allolobophora icterica* (Savigny) (oligochète Lombricien). *Mém. Soc. linn. Normandie* (N.S.) Zool. **3** No. 1, 5–158.

Savigny, J. C. 1826. [La multiplicité des espèces de ver de terre] *Mem. Acad. Sci. Inst. Fr.* (Phys.) **5**, 176–184.

Schwert, D. P. 1979. Description and significance of a fossil earthworm (Oligochaeta: Lumbricidae) cocoon from post glacial sediments in southern Ontario. Can. J. Zool. **57**(7), 1402–1405.

Segun, A. O. 1971. Acephaline gregarines of earthworms—additions to the British records. *J. Protozool.* **18**, 313–317.

Service, R. 1890. Note on *Perichaeta indica,* an exotic species of earthworm living in hothouses in Kirkcudbrightshire. *Proc. R. phys. Soc. Edinb.* **10**, 396–398.

Sims, R. W. 1973. *Lumbricus terrestris* Linnaeus, 1758 (Annelida, Oligochaeta): designation of a neotype in accordance with accustomed usage. Problems arising from the misidentification of the species by Savigny (1822 & 1826). *Z. N.(S)* 272. *Bull. zool. Nomencl.* **30**(1), 27–33.

Sims, R. W. 1980. A classification and the distribution of earthworms, suborder Lumbricina (Haplotaxida: Oligochaeta). *Bull. Br. Mus. nat. Hist.* (Zool.) **39**(2), 103–124.

Sims, R. W. 1982a. Revision of the eastern African earthworm genus *Polytoreutus* (Eudrilidae: Oligochaeta). *Bull. Br. Mus. nat. Hist.* (Zool.) **43**(5), 253–298.

Sims, R. W. 1982b. Lumbricina. In *Synopsis and classification of living organisms*, ed. Parker, S. P. **2**, 55–61. New York: McGraw-Hill.

Sims, R. W. 1983. The scientific names of earthworms. In *Earthworm ecology from Darwin to vermiculture*, ed. Satchell, J. E., pp. 467–474. London: Chapman and Hall.

Sims, R. W. and Easton, E. G. 1972. A numerical revision of the earthworm genus *Pheretima* auct. (Megascolecidae: Oligochaeta) with the recognition of new genera and an appendix on the earthworms collected by the Royal Society North Borneo Expedition. *Biol. J. Linn. Soc.* **4**(3), 169–268.

Southwood, T. R. E. 1979. *Ecological methods: with particular reference to the study of insect populations* 324 pp. London: Chapman and Hall.

Spencer, B. 1900. Further descriptions of Australian earthworms, Part I. *Proc. R. Soc. Vict.* (N.S.) **13**, 29–67.

Stephenson, J. 1930. *The Oligochaeta.* 978 pp. Oxford: Oxford University Press.

Støp-Bovitz, C. 1969. A contribution to our knowledge of the systematics and zoogeography of Norwegian earthworms (Annelida Oligochaeta: Lumbricidae). *Nytt Mag. Zool.* **17**(2), 170–280.

Svendsen, J. A. 1956. The oöthecae of four species of British Lumbricidae. *Ann. Mag. nat. Hist.* Ser. 12 **9**, 730–732.

Terhivuo, J. 1982. Relative efficiency of hand-sorting, formalin application and combination of both methods in extracting Lumbricidae from Finnish soils. *Pedobiologia* **23**, 175–188.

Tétry, A. 1934. Description d'une espèce française du genre *Pelodrilus. C. R. Acad. Sci. Paris* **199**, 322–324.

Tétry, A. 1937. Révision des lombriciens de la collection de Savigny. *Bull. Mus. natn. Hist. nat.* **9**(2), 140–155.

Tomlin, A. D. and Miller, J. J. 1980. Development and fecundity of the manure worm, *Eisenia fetida* (Annelida: Lumbricidae), under laboratory conditions. In *Soil biology as related to land use practices. Proceedings of the VII International Colloquium of Soil Zoology*, ed. Dindal, D. L. pp. 673–678. Washington, Environmental Protection Agency.

Ude, H. 1885. Ueber die Rückenporen der terricolen Oligochaeten, nebst Beiträgen zur Histologie des Leibesschlauches und zur Systematik der Lumbriciden. *Z. wiss. Zool.* **43**, 87–143.

Vaillant, L. 1868. Note sur l'anatomie de deux espèces du genre *Perichaeta* et essai de classification des Annélides Lombricines. *Annls. Sci. nat.* **10**, 225–256 and *Mem. Acad. Sci. Lett. Montpelier* **7**, 143–173.

Wallwork, J. A. 1983. *Earthworm biology.* The Institute of Biology's Studies in Biology no. 161. 58 pp. London: Edward Arnold.

Wood, T. G. 1974. The distribution of earthworms (Megascolecidae) in relation to soils, vegetation and altitude on the slopes of Mt. Kosciusko, Australia. *J. anim. Ecol.* **43**, 87–106.

Zicsi, A. 1978. Revision der Art *Dendrobaena platyura* (Fitzinger, 1833) (Oligochaeta: Lumbricidae). *Acta zool. hung.* **24**, 439–449.

Zicsi, A. 1981. Weitere Angaben zur Lumbriciden fauna Italiens (Oligochaeta: Lumbricidae). *Opusc. Zool. Budapest* **17/18**, 157–180.

Zicsi, A. 1982. Verzeichnis der bis 1971 beschreibenen und revidierten Taxa der Familie Lumbricidae. *Acta zool. hung.* **28**(3–4), 421–454.

Index of scientific names

Valid names of genera and species are printed in *italic* type and names listed in synonymy are printed in roman type; higher group names are printed in CAPITAL LETTERS. The page number of the principal reference to a name is printed in **bold** type whereas the page numbers of subsidiary references are printed in roman type.